long term

It aims to
the politi
quality of

This book is due for re

I0581234

N.

Demos publishes books and ...   ...undertakes substantial empirical and policy-oriented research projects. Demos is a registered charity. In all its work Demos brings together people from a wide range of backgrounds in business, academia, government, the voluntary sector and the media to share and cross-fertilise ideas and experiences.

The Carnegie Young People Initiative aims to improve the quality and increase the breadth of the involvement of young people aged 10 to 25 in public decision-making. It is doing this in three ways – mapping what is happening, promoting the evaluation of good practice and developing standards for the public and voluntary sectors at national and local levels to involve young people. The initiative was set up in 1996 by the Carnegie UK Trust and actively promotes young people's involvement in its own work as well as that of other partners.

For further information and subscription details please contact:
Demos
The Mezzanine
Elizabeth House
39 York Road
London SE1 7NQ
telephone: 020 7401 5330
email: mail@demos.co.uk
www.demos.co.uk,

Logged off?

How ICT can connect young people and politics

Lydia Howland

with Matthew Bethell

DEMOS

First published in 2002 by
Demos
The Mezzanine
Elizabeth House
39 York Road
London SE1 7NQ

ISBN 1 84180 049 X
Typeset by Politico's Design, design@politicos.co.uk
Printed in Britain by PIMS

Contents

About the authors

Lydia Howland joined Demos in August 2001 as a researcher, having graduated from Cardiff University with a degree in English and cultural criticism. Since joining Demos, she has been investigating the issues surrounding young people's participation in political issues and the debate around e-government and the implications of using new technologies within the democratic process.

Matthew Bethell joined Demos on a three-month internship in September 2001, having completed his A levels. After leaving Demos he travelled to Ghana to work as a teacher and educational adviser in the Abrafo-Odumasi province. Matt has regularly worked as a youth play-worker at a children's playground in London, so his main interests lie in youth work and young people's engagement with politics. When he returns to the UK this autumn, Matt will be taking up his place at Cambridge University to study social and political science.

Acknowledgements

The authors would like to thank the Carnegie Young People Initiative, particularly David Cutler, Kylie Kilgour, Sara Bryson and Ravi Gurumurthy, for their input, advice and feedback. Thanks also to all at Demos, especially Daniel Stedman Jones, Matthew Horne, Rachel Jupp, Eddie Gibb and Tom Bentley. Thanks are also due to all the people who have helped shape the direction of this report or contributed to its findings. In particular, we would like to thank Ann Mackintosh, Amar Abass, Maria Javed, Steve Waterhouse, Guy Rubin, Matt Milliken and Andrew Struck for their help in compiling the case studies.

The report analyses the major issues associated with using ICTs in this context, and illustrates them through detailed case studies of projects that engage young people in a range of ways. The issues are:

- *Apathy*
  How should the terms of young people's political disengagement really be understood?

- *Access*
  What needs to be available, and on what terms, in order for ICTs to serve young people's engagement fairly and effectively?

- *Safety*
  What risks do ICTs and the internet present to young people, and how can they be managed?

- *Empowerment*
  What does an overall commitment to empowering and supporting young people in engaging with politics and society involve?

The report concludes with a series of recommendations for policy and practice.

Democracy is based on the idea of engagement in dialogue and decision-making between equals, yet for young people something is lost between the rhetoric and the reality. Without the franchise, efforts to engage those aged under 18 rarely amount to more than tokenism. Inviting young people to take part in consultation exercises or sit on youth forums pays lip service to promoting participation but frequently fails to deliver. ICTs can enable young people to engage with adults on more equal terms and reduce some of the inequalities of power, self-expression and access that currently hinder their public involvement. For example, our case studies show that the anonymity of the internet can encourage young people to express politically sensitive or contentious issues that might not be brought out in face-to-face situations. It can also neutralise some of the advantages associated with age, race, faith, gender, ability and background. Anonymity can help to build confidence and empowerment, but exploiting ICTs to promote this is a staging post and not a long-term solution in itself.

The ultimate goal is to create a climate in which the input of young people is not only valued, but also translated into genuine influence and responsibility. ICTs could be instrumental in achieving this, but to be effective they require a strong underlying commitment to promoting young people's participation in public life. This means that individuals and organisations will have to reconfigure their relationship to young people and incorporate them into systems and processes previously reserved for adults. It will involve recognition across all sectors of public life that young people are entitled to make an input into the mechanisms that govern them and that, if their opinions are to be canvassed, then their responses cannot be ignored.

Our research shows that many young people are developing innovative and more relevant ways of using technology to empower themselves and engage with political culture. Our case studies show that in many cases young people have been quick to capitalise on the principles of interaction made possible by ICTs. They are using them to share knowledge, power and responsibility across networks, often in ways that preserve their informality and flexibility. In the light of these examples, the bigger question becomes: How might these developments help to change civic culture and the wider opportunities offered by governance to citizens and young people?

Ultimately, ICTs must become the tool for changing the identity of political institutions themselves. ICT initiatives that are better designed and used strategically rather than simply being 'bolted on' as prosthetics should help enable the kind of organisational renewal necessary to endow political systems with relevance and meaning. This applies not just to young people, but for the whole of a rapidly changing society.

2. 'Apathy'?

Voter turnout has reached the lowest level since universal suffrage was introduced in 1918, prompting unprecedented concern and analysis among politicians, sociologists, trends analysts and the media. The Electoral Commission is currently running a high-profile advertising campaign urging people to register to vote; the BBC has established a review to examine how political news can attract a wider range of viewers and listeners; and the government has appointed three separate task forces to examine the problem.

Voter turnout and membership of political parties have decreased across every age bracket, except for those over 55, proving it is not only the young who feel distanced from the mechanisms of governance or alienated from politics. Yet young people's supposed 'apathy' attracts attention because of the serious implications it has for the future. Not only are adults 'switching off', but the fear is now that young people are not being 'switched on' in the first place. As a consequence, one of the three government-appointed task forces is specifically charged with investigating political apathy among the young. In a society where more people voted for Will and Gareth in *Pop Idol* than for the Conservative Party during the last general election, fears are mounting about the future of Britain's representative democracy.

The media frequently dismiss young people as entirely apathetic towards politics. Figures show not only that fewer young people are voting, but also that a smaller number of them have firm allegiances to political parties or even trade unions. This report argues that 'apathy' is actually a misnomer for a malaise that would be better understood as disempowerment from the formal mechanisms through which politics is organised.

The proliferation of school councils and youth parliaments within the last 10 to 15 years all testify to a growing, not declining, interest in politics and decision-making. The rights of young people are enshrined in Article 12 of the UN Convention on the Rights of the Child and young people throughout the world have established Article 12 campaigning organisations to help protect this right. Interest in volunteering has also increased and involvement with civil society remains strong. At the moment there are 60,000 young people registered to join the Scouting and Girl Guide movement, but they are forced to wait because there are not sufficient numbers of adults prepared to run the clubs.[1] Many young people view the existing political system, in which parties and parliamentary institutions are positioned at the centre of an increasingly complex political spectrum, as anachronistic. The political issues they care about differ from the concerns of previous generations, yet formal political institutions are not perceived as reflecting this shift.

The challenge for government and politicians, local decision-makers, teachers, parents and the media is to endow political structures with a meaning for young people before they reach voting age. The citizenship curriculum, due to come into effect from September 2002, will help to promote young people's roles as citizens, but on its own it is unlikely dramatically to alter the disillusionment with the existing system.

Easy assertions

The 1997 general election turnout figures show that the 18–24 age bracket was far less politically motivated than its middle-aged counterpart.[2] Significantly, however, a survey conducted by Charter 88 revealed that over 91 per cent of young people would be more likely to vote if parties addressed issues that mattered to them.[3] Arguably, therefore, it is not that young people are uninterested in political ideas, but that formal politics isn't interested in young people or reflective of the issues that affect them.[4]

In the 2001 general election the turnout fell to a mere 59 per cent, from 71 per cent in 1997. pointing to a far broader political disengagement.[5]

Why bother to change how 'Apathy' is measured?

The traditional model for measuring young people's political disengagement has become severely outdated. The declining numbers of young people affiliated to a political party may tell us something about the changing relationship between young people and traditional political identities, but they fail to reflect the growth in single-issue politics and membership of non-governmental organisations. These measures offer little or no assessment of the wider political issues that affect and concern young people.

We need a more sophisticated method of evaluating young people's attitudes towards politics.[6] Only by defining a model that makes a greater effort to understand where young people's political interest and involvement lies will we be able to measure the true extent of their engagement.

ICTs as tools for promoting engagement

Politics is pervasive. It ranges from the goings-on in Westminster to community debates about tackling racism, and it extends to global organisations rallying against the onslaught of capitalism and multinational corporations. Technology is similarly pervasive. Mobile phones are ubiquitous, the internet spans the globe and entertainment-based applications are now global. Technology can provide more efficient and autonomous ways of communicating with decision-makers and ensuring that young people's opinions and suggestions are incorporated into decision-making. The work of the International Teledemocracy Centre shows how the internet can be used, not only to promote engagement with existing institutions, but also to create new arrangements better designed to serve the needs of young people.

The International Teledemocracy Centre and the Highland Youth Voice Elections

The International Teledemocracy Centre (ITC) was set up in 1999 at Napier University in association with British Telecom to examine how best to develop and deploy technologies in order to encourage participation in political life.

The Highland Youth Voice pilot initiative was launched in the Highlands of Scotland, and aimed to reconnect young people with politics as well as to showcase practical applications of e-voting technologies. The Highland communities have a population of around 280,000 but are hugely dispersed over a vast and often remote area. In a bid to connect and represent those in the Highland communities better, a council was established to include a youth parliament that would help to encourage greater participation among young people in the area.

In conjunction with BT, the ITC piloted an e-voting initiative whereby young people could vote for their youth parliament members online. All the schools in the Highland area were invited to take part in the scheme, but were also given the option of electing representatives via a traditional paper ballot. Of the 29 secondary schools that took part, about one-third took part online, a further third opted for the traditional paper ballot, and the final third had unopposed candidates standing, negating the need for an election altogether.

A website was created (www.highlandyouthvoice.org), which became the focal point for all communications in the run-up to, and during, the election. The candidates posted their manifestos and election pledges online, and the students were able to make discussion board postings on a diverse range of topics.

On the day of the election, the students were given a secure numerical pin code, which enabled them to log on to the site and cast their vote. In terms of the wider e-voting context, it was a successful pilot, which left a working prototype for future e-elections. The results were finalised very quickly, with one school proclaiming it had taken half the time to process them than had originally been expected. Significantly, a higher percentage of people voted in schools using the electronic ballot as opposed to schools using a paper ballot, suggesting that use of ICTs had increased levels of engagement and participation.

Having elected the executive for the youth parliament, the original website is now redundant. It is still possible to view some of the discussion boards and the results of the election, but no part of the content remains 'live'. However, anxious that this should be a sustained initiative that builds on the success of the original pilot, the ITC and the elected youth executive have now developed an entirely new site. This will become the focal point for the next round of elections, due to take place in October 2002.

Unlike the original site, the new one (still at the same web address – www.highlandyouthvoice.org) has been designed and maintained entirely by young people themselves, ensuring they have total ownership and editorial authority over content. The site continues to focus on interactivity by hosting online debates and posting the feedback from them on the website, and by putting users in touch with their elected representatives.

The Highland Youth Voice election demonstrates that not all young people are 'apathetic' towards the more formal aspects of politics. In fact, they are even willing to replicate existing political formats providing they are designed to serve the agenda of young people and can deliver a degree of purchase over the people and institutions that matter. The Highland Youth Council is based on a traditional model of governance but has reapplied it in a different context to demonstrate the relevance of political engagement.

Ann Mackintosh argues that young people are an obvious choice for an initiative because they are generally more receptive to doing things differently:

> Unlike adults, young people do not see going to the polling station and casting a paper ballot as part of their civic duty. They are not burdened by a nostalgic fondness for how things used to be, and have no inherent loyalty to the concept of a polling booth.

As a generation, young people are far more accustomed to using information and communication technologies to enable them to perform basic functions, and see voting as no exception. Significantly, in schools using the electronic online voting system, a higher percentage of students used their vote, suggesting that this method of voting had an impact on levels of engagement and participation. Online voting also allowed the results to be processed far more quickly than would be possible in a paper ballot, and with a greater degree of security and accuracy.

The Highland Youth Voice website (www.highlandyouthvoice.org) enabled young people to create a virtual, online community far less disparate than the geographical one in which they live. Nearly 30 secondary schools took part, creating virtual links between students and teachers that would not have been possible otherwise. Students standing for election were able to respond to issues, creating a dialogue between the candidates and their electorate that isn't always possible in traditional politics.

Although the organisers had hoped to involve young people in the creation of the original site, initial funding was limited and, consequently, it was designed entirely by adults. Now that the Highland Youth Council has its elected members and is fully operational, the executive has built a brand new site to supersede the previous one, designed entirely by young people themselves. It features an online debating chamber, which is peer-moderated. Debates are summarised and posted back on to the site, together with details of any decisions or actions that may be taken as a result. It also includes a 'news feed' so that relevant news articles can be submitted for inclusion on the site. Crucially, the new website gives high visibility and prominence to changes in policy instigated by the youth executive, in order to increase awareness among the electorate of the goals and outcomes achieved by their representatives.

The International Teledemocracy Centre has succeeded in organising an e-voting initiative that not only encouraged students in the Highlands to engage with political issues via ICTs but also, in doing so, created a youth executive with democratic legitimacy.

Net-based and networked

ICTs can be used to create entirely new organisational frameworks and to diversify the ways in which young people can participate in civil society. One such example is the Millennium Volunteers scheme.

Millennium Volunteers

Millennium Volunteers is a government-funded initiative that aims to increase volunteering among young people. Members of the scheme give up their time to help others by doing something that they already enjoy (such as sport, music or drama) within their local community. The scheme is open to anyone aged between 16 and 24, and those who take part gain experience, confidence and skills as a result of the projects they have been involved with. There have been 43,000 Millennium Volunteers on the scheme since 1999 and there are currently around 20,000 volunteers working in over 180 different projects nationwide.

Projects range from sports coaching to youth leadership, but all participants have the freedom to choose which projects they become involved with. Of those registered with the scheme, 58 per cent have never volunteered previously, which suggests fairly strongly that young people are not irreversibly 'apathetic' but are actually very willing to become more involved participants in civil society.[7] Millennium Volunteers also gain some of the skills that employers value, such as working as part of a team, learning to solve problems and developing their own initiative. A certificate is given to volunteers after contributing 100 hours, and then an Award of Excellence, signed by the Secretary of State for the Department for Education and Skills, is awarded to those going on to complete 200 hours in a year.

The Millennium Volunteers scheme also promotes autonomy and decision-making within its structure. Amar Abass is Chairperson of the National Youth Forum, which aims to represent the views of all Millennium Volunteers nationwide. The forum is made up of 18 young people who either are or have been volunteers on the scheme themselves. There are nine regional youth forums, comprising a collection of local projects, and each of these regional forums selects two members to represent their views nationally. The National Forum meets four times a year and the views and suggestions of its members are relayed to the national unit within the DfES in order to influence national policy. The organisational structure of the scheme means that young people not only volunteer within their local communities but also have the opportunity to become more involved with the scheme's governance by participating in the regional and national forums.

As the scheme is government-funded, it has its own website (www.millenniumvolunteers.gov.uk), which is linked to the central DfES site. One of the policy changes the National Forum was able to instigate was the creation of a new website as the general consensus among the forum members was that the original site was unambitious, drab and not striking the right tone. Maria Javed, the National Forum's communications officer, was asked to present the views of Millennium Volunteers to the DfES and she highlighted concerns about the content of the original site and its accessibility. The site involved very few contributions from Volunteers themselves, and it was thought to be difficult to navigate to the site from the DfES homepage.

The panel responded to some of Maria's concerns, demonstrating a commitment by the scheme's organisers to incorporate the suggestions of the forum members. The current site now provides a lot more information about the scheme and the kinds of projects that volunteers are currently involved with. It also contains profiles of current volunteers as well as details of how to join the scheme. Although most members of the youth forums concede that the current site is an improvement on the original, Maria still thought that a more engaging site could be designed, which could be used to support the Millennium Volunteers nation-wide and encourage greater interaction between members. She therefore created her own Millennium Volunteers website (www.millenniumvolunteers.org.uk), which effectively acts as an alternative site for the scheme.

The Millennium Volunteers scheme shows that many young people are willing to make a contribution to civic society at a much more local, 'grass roots' level. It is also notable for being a fairly successful central government-led initiative. It has attracted a lot of young people on to the scheme. The creation of a national forum highlights an underlying commitment to youth involvement at all levels of the programme.

However, the shortcomings of the scheme are evident in the approach of the DfES to the use of ICTs. Although Millennium Volunteers has tried to update its website in response to the suggestions from National Forum members, it has failed to make full use of what internet tech-nology can offer. Ultimately, it was Maria Javed's unilateral action in creating an 'alternative' site that showed how the internet could become a real focal point for the scheme and 'virtually' enhance the 'actual' networks that exist among the projects and volunteers.

The Millennium Volunteers scheme is heavily network-based. In order to operate successfully, it requires volunteers to communicate regularly with each other and the people in charge of the projects. But the official website only features one interactive component – a voting tool about whether volunteering is cool or not. There are no links to any of the satellite pages that have been set up by the regional forums. Even the case studies that profile existing volunteers are written in the third person (for instance, Cathy is 21 and from Liverpool) so hardly any of the site's content belongs to the volunteers themselves. The official website remains little more than information provider.

By contrast, www.millenniumvolunteers.org.uk – the site created by Maria Javed to serve the Greater Manchester regional forum – exploits the possibilities the internet can offer much more fully. The use of tech-nology is not revolutionary, it simply involves message boards and shared information resources, but there is also the opportunity for users to join up as 'cyber MVs'. This site is a more effective support tool and connection point than the main site because the interactive forums help to reinforce and sustain existing networks. The Greater

Manchester site highlights a different way of organising networks of people and promoting participation.

Lessons to be learned

When used in innovative and interactive ways, ICTs can reduce some of the disappointments that young people experience in relation to political engagement and decision-making and make existing institutions more accessible. Many young people gain confidence when sitting in front of a monitor, which they do not have when sitting in front of a room full of adults.

The speed and efficiency of technology can make a very practical difference. Yet, even if the real problem is a deeper sense of disenfranchisement, ICTs may still be able to help, if there is already a commitment to young people's participation.

The factor that appears critical to the success of any ICT strategy is giving young people ownership of such initiatives by allowing them to design the content and manage the outcomes. The trend so far has been for decision-makers to use technology as a quick way of canvassing the views of young people, by use of email surveys and questionnaires. If the responses are not then translated into tangible outcomes on behalf of those young people who participated, they are unlikely to have a lasting impact. Technology can not only give people of all ages more opportunities to engage with the existing political structures, but also allow for the creation of new ones.

Although the case studies highlight ways in which formal politics and involvement with civic society have been invigorated by creative use of ICTs, the disillusionment with politics is too widespread to be rectified by a few isolated initiatives. Technology is certainly capable of helping to engage young people with political agendas, but this relies on young people first having access to the necessary technologies. The next chapter examines the issue of access further.

Websites of interest

www.highlandyouthvoice.org
www.itc.org.uk
www.millenniumvolunteers.gov.uk
www.millenniumvolunteers.org.uk

3. Access

While they may, in the long run, be revolutionary, the price and complexity of new technologies have the power to exclude, especially young people. While a mobile phone is increasingly seen as a necessary expense, financing a personal computer with an internet connection is still well beyond the budget of most young people. Schools are by far the most widespread providers of ICT facilities to young people, but they can only provide limited access within an institutionalised environment.

The government is committed to bridging the 'digital divide', for example by offering an email address to every young person by 2005 and opening UK Online centres. But access is more than just contact with technology. Making the most of what it can offer young people depends on access to hardware, but also to 'mindware'.[8] 'Mindware' refers to the skills and techniques necessary to make the most of all the content and opportunities available online.

A recent report suggests that as many as 33 million people in the UK regularly go online.[9] The computer sales industry recently reported its first slump in online take-up rates, but access to and use of ICTs is more and more commonplace, particularly at home.[10] Crucially, however, the distribution of this access is not equal across socioeconomic groups. Over 65 per cent of middle-class children have access to a personal computer in the home, compared with just 40 per cent of working-class children. Some 14 per cent of middle-class children can go online at home, compared with a mere 2 per cent of their working-class counterparts.[11] Inequalities of access are partly redressed by UK Online centres, libraries, youth clubs, City Learning Centres and schools, but not all young people find educational institutions conducive to making the most of the facilities available. UK online centres and City Learning Centres do not actively target the 11–24-year age group. The challenge, therefore, is to provide young people with access in environments that enables them to use new technologies to their fullest potential. One initiative that has demonstrably achieved this is the Interchill cyber drop-in centre in Liverpool.

Interchill

Interchill is a cyber drop-in centre that provides free internet access, educational resources, career advice and counselling to people aged between 11 and 25 in the Speke and Garston area of Merseyside. The area receives European regeneration funding, almost 40 per cent of the population is under 25 and over a quarter of known offenders are aged 18 or under. According to project manager Steve Waterhouse, most adults who live in the area identify children and young people as the causes of vandalism, noise and nuisance behaviour. Interchill aims to redress this perception by giving young people a facility that not only keeps them off the streets but allows them to demonstrate they are willing and capable decision-makers, participants and stakeholders in their local community.

Interchill's ethos is to promote 'empowerment, inclusion, participation and citizenship'. The centre's annual trustees' report states: '[t]he aim of the Interchill project is to help and educate young people through their leisure-time activities – to develop their physical, mental and spiritual capacities so that they may grow to full maturity as individuals and members of society and so that their conditions of life may be improved'. In practice, this means providing a facility where anyone aged between 11 and 25 from the local area can use the centre to access the internet free of charge, receive counselling, career advice, training in ICT use, do their homework, organise meetings and events or simply meet up socially with friends.

Underpinning the commitment to participation is Interchill's organisational structure. The centre has deliberately adopted a fairly hierarchical and bureaucratic approach to management but, unlike many other organisations that follow this model, it places young people's participation at the centre of the process. The centre's 12 trustees are themselves aged between 18 and 25, are elected annually and have full legal responsibility for the project. A smaller group of trustees also runs the personnel sub-committee, which meets with the centre's staff monthly. The management committee also meets monthly to discuss the project's direction and to receive reports from the chairman, treasurer and from the two representatives from the junior committee, which meets twice monthly and is responsible for the day-to-day running of the project. Young people are instrumental in the governance of the centre at every level.

Another tenet central to Interchill's ethos is the provision of free internet access. The centre offers a state-of-the-art ICT suite, complete with scanners and CD writers, enabling Interchill members to access technologies which may not be available to them at home, or to which they have limited access at school. The centre runs a homework club in addition to designated sessions for 11–13-year-olds, and for 14–25-year-olds in which members can use the internet to research school projects, chat online, download music or send emails.

Interchill's real triumph has been to use free internet access as a way of giving local young people access to people and situations they may otherwise have been excluded from. Not only can members physically access ICTs, but they are encouraged to use them to access local decision-makers via online conferences organised by the project workers. The work being done at Interchill demonstrates that access to hardware, combined with access to figures of authority, encourages young people who might otherwise be socially excluded to participate in debate and public decision-making. Interchill's approach is distinctive because it allows them to do so on their own terms and through technologies they enjoy using in an environment that they have total ownership of.

Provision of free internet access for young people was one of the main reasons for creating Interchill. According to project manager Steve Waterhouse:

> Interchill is used by kids who rarely use ICTs. The trick that we've pulled off is creating an environment where young people want to use IT, they know the staff, they know the environment, they're comfortable, feel safe and therefore feel able to ask . . . when they want to access information.

Steve Waterhouse believes that, when confronted by too much formal training and technical jargon, young people become deterred from using ICTs because they don't feel they are doing so on their own terms. As he observes:

> If you said that's what we're doing – 'web browsing', 'file conversion', 'downloading files' and 'digital formatting' – the young people we are working with simply wouldn't go and do it. Formal education and assessment are a no-no.

Interchill's ability to attract young people to ICTs hinges largely on its users' sense of ownership over the facilities it offers young people, which not only increases the level of use, but also increases confidence in using new technologies. As Lizzy, a regular user aged 16, from Garston, Liverpool, states:

> In the Homework Club, I do my research for school projects, because I have no computer at home . . . someone told me about Interchill, so I got myself a membership and since then my grades in school have increased to Bs, all thanks to Interchill's cool ICT room and relaxed area to concentrate in.

The facilities have also provided its users with access to people and organisations the young people might otherwise never have encountered. Seeing the potential of the internet for engaging young people in political debate, Steve Waterhouse organised an online conference called 'Chatback'. Using the centre's facilities, a group of 18 Interchill members took part in an online discussion with two Liverpool city councillors. Aware that none of the young people participating had ever talked to local decision-makers before, Steve would provide a virtual space for young people to engage in constructive discussions with them. As he says:

> [T]he good thing about doing it over a chat room is that the councillors can't make judgments about the young people based on age, gender, race, class, look, dress or any of those things . . . [E]qually, the young people are not put off by a 55-year-old bloke in a suit in a very formal environment. They would not have asked the same questions of those people in another context. In

another setting, that dialogue and the level of discussion would not have been the same because the inhibitors to it would have been too strong.

Steve proudly points out that several members of Interchill have become involved with external organisations, including South Liverpool Housing and UK Youth Parliament and as trainee learning mentors in local schools.

Interchill's achievements are threefold. First, the governance and management of the centre are influenced directly by its members, giving them genuine opportunities to participate in the decision-making process. Second, Interchill provides free access to the internet within an environment that appeals to young people. Third, Interchill provides access not just to hardware, but also to people and opportunities that might not normally be available to its users.

Mind-ware

Recent research shows that younger children in particular are quite conservative in their use of the internet, visiting only a few sites and often not straying beyond the home page.[12] This evidence suggests that although access to the hardware is not always a problem, knowing how to access the variety of material available online is a major challenge.

The National Curriculum for ICT in schools aims to provide young people with basic levels of technology literacy. It encourages pupils to 'use ICT tools effectively to share, exchange and present information',[13] and acknowledges the enormous potential that ICTs offer:

> Increased capability in the use of ICT promotes initiative and independent learning, with pupils being able to make informed judgments about when and where to use ICTs to best effect, and to consider its implications for home and work both now and in the future.[14]

At Key Stage 3, young people are expected to know 'how to use ICT including email to share and exchange information effectively . . . working with others to explore a variety of information sources and ICT tools in a variety of contexts'. At Key Stage 4, they are expected to 'reflect critically on the impact of ICT on their own and others' lives, considering the social, economic, political, legal, ethical and moral issues.[15] The curriculum aims to familiarise young people with multi-media applications such as CD-Roms, databases, videos and adventure games, but what is notably absent is a strategy for introducing them to the e-possibilities that exist. If young people are genuinely to explore the possibilities the internet can offer and (within reason) use it to set and pursue their own agendas, they also need to know how to access the online resources that will allow them to make the most of these opportunities. Currently, the ways that pupils are introduced to the potential of ICTs is left to the discretion of individual schools and teachers.

The one-way information superhighway

The emphasis of the National Curriculum for ICT means that, in practice, the internet is seldom more than a one-way information superhighway. Although schools are obliged to let all students make use of the internet, the focus is invariably on using it to extract information as opposed to encouraging opportunities for participation and engagement. For example, many chatroom sites are prohibited by firewalls, despite the fact they could be used to promote constructive discussions. ICTs, and in particular the internet, offer enormous scope for reciprocity and interaction. Most schools which are answerable to the National Curriculum have been reluctant to capitalise on this.

One initiative that has been innovative in providing young people with access to ICTs and participatory processes is in the London Borough of Lewisham.

London Borough of Lewisham

In 1995 Guy Rubin worked at the London Borough of Lewisham Council on 'Lewisham Listens', a project intended to address the growing 'democratic deficit' between government, public services and the citizens they aim to serve.

In 1997 an evaluation of the project suggested that Lewisham Council should pilot new technologies as a way of engaging and involving young people in the borough, giving them a more participatory role in civic society and public decision-making. This developed into a project that aimed to use technology as a means for facilitating the connection of young people to the workings of the council by providing maximum youth involvement and a 'bottom up' approach. The intention was not simply to canvass the opinions of young people but actually to incorporate their responses into new policy directives.

The project was initially launched in local primary schools and students were asked to design their own questionnaire to identify what they perceived to be the key issues facing them as young residents in Lewisham. The best questions from the various submissions were collated and the finalised questionnaire was delivered to every primary school in the borough. Most questionnaires were sent out via online technologies, but the lack of ICT facilities in some schools meant that hard copies had to accompany the electronic version. Crucially, completion of the questionnaire became an activity that was integrated into the existing ICT curriculum requirements, meaning that every child of primary school age participated in the exercise. The results and their analysis were published online by the pupils themselves, with a select group later invited to attend a council meeting and present their findings directly to the councillors. The design and distribution of the questionnaire has now become an annual process, generating almost 1,000 responses from local young people.

Acknowledging the responses from the questionnaires, in which students claimed to feel removed from the workings of local government, Lewisham Council hosted a conference for primary and secondary students in the borough. It sought to explain the role of the council and why it was relevant to local young people. As a result of these discussions, the council set up a bullying website and hosted an online conference on the topic. The discussion board generated around 200 messages, and the site itself received over 6,000 hits during the time it was live – an overwhelming response given the size of the youth population of the borough.

Another initiative, launched by the council in 2000, was called 'Your Vote – Your Choice'. Having identified £10,000 within its education budget, the council invited students to generate ideas for projects that would benefit young people in Lewisham, which the council would then fund. Once all ideas had been tendered a shortlist of three was drawn up and students submitted their vote for the best initiative via electronic voting machines. This allowed the council to generate immediate results for individual schools across the borough. The project that won was an idea to produce a CD-Rom on racism, to be accompanied by a teaching resources and production pack.

Lewisham Council aims to build on the success of these initiatives by using ICTs within the school curriculum to show young people how they can be used as tools for participation. Using schools' ICT facilities ensures maximum numbers of young people are able to participate, and no one's views are excluded because they haven't access to the internet at home or in their leisure time. In addition to this, it helped to increase young people's awareness of the potential of ICTs by giving them access to a variety of applications that enabled them to participate in broadly political debates and gave them some influence on local decision-makers.

Lewisham Councillors run the 'Lewisham Listens' initiative annually to help sustain the interest in participation that the initial project generated.

Lewisham's approach to youth consultation is markedly different from most similar exercises for two key reasons. First, rather than adults and councillors posing the questions, local schoolchildren were asked to devise the questionnaire themselves, giving them total ownership of the content. Second, once the results had been collated they were published and presented by young people and the results were taken as a starting point for new initiatives, such as the website on bullying and the 'Your Vote – Your Choice' programme. This commitment to feedback and reciprocity underpins Lewisham Council's approach to young people; adults in authority are determined to ensure that consultation exercises are not tokenistic and that the views and responses submitted by children have a genuine impact on subsequent policies and decisions.

ICTs, therefore, are not solely responsible for the high levels of participation and engagement among Lewisham's youth. But this case study shows that ICTs can be used in a variety of ways to encourage participation because they allow young people to own the process and the content of what they produce. The findings of the initial survey were collated easily and published online, so that participants could see the results posted on the same site that they had visited to complete the questionnaire. The internet is well disposed to provide reciprocity and feedback because of the speed of the technology and the opportunities for interaction.

'Lewisham Listens' proves that it is possible to use ICTs to encourage young people to participate in public decision-making, and to do so as part of the National Curriculum. Access to ICTs is allocated fairly equally within schools – a fact the organisers capitalised on to ensure that as many local school children took part in the project as possible. But this project also went a step further by giving young people access to a variety of techniques and applications that made them aware of the potential implications of emerging technologies, particularly in the context of political engagement and citizenship.

Lessons learned

Lack of access to hardware is not the only obstacle preventing young people from making the most of what technology can offer. The inability to access the range of materials and opportunities available on the internet, especially in the context of political engagement, participation and public decision-making, needs to be addressed. While the National Curriculum acknowledges that young people should learn to consider the social and political implications of new technologies, there is no 'joined-up' framework for actually achieving this.

Yet ultimately the difference that ICTs can make to young people's political engagement hinges on a very different notion of access. The internet is a particularly powerful tool because it provides access to people and organisations that young people traditionally have little or no contact with. The internet can be and is being used to make the mechanisms of governance more accessible, and online discussions, surveys and conferences give young people the opportunity to put their views before the people and institutions that count.

The internet can also make feedback far easier to deliver. Online discussions, conferences and noticeboards give users access to the outcomes of consultation exercises. Views can be exchanged and debated rather than simply put forward in a one-way flow of information. The net can create a virtual dialogue in a way that is often difficult or impossible to achieve in real life.

There are, however, growing concerns among adults that the internet makes it too easy for young people to access inappropriate material and, more worryingly, for the wrong kind of adults to gain access to young people. Although new technologies are often cited as drivers for change, there are instances in which they can become barriers. Concerns about access are inextricably bound up with issues of safety, and these fears are sometimes used as justification for curtailing young people's access to the internet. These issues are discussed in the following chapter.

Websites of interest
www.interchill.co.uk
ecs.lewisham.gov.uk/citizens/

4. Safety

There are mounting concerns among adults that the internet is an unsafe medium for young people to use. A number of cases in which young people's safety has been compromised as a consequence of online interactions have received high-profile media attention and spurred lobbying of the government for better online protection of young people. The Labour government's initial response to the problem has been swift, but a wider debate continues about the need to reconcile demands for censorship with the need to promote risk management and access.

This chapter explores the dangers that anonymity and exposure to inappropriate material can pose to young people, examines current efforts to minimise the risk, and identifies the remaining obstacles to making the internet a genuinely safe environment for young people. It will also consider the ways in which the safety of young people online has been used as a smokescreen for censorship, and the problems this can create as well as solve.

Young people's safety while online is not at risk when their use is social, for example in chatrooms. A survey conducted in June 2001 found that just over 51 per cent of all chatroom users were aged under 24.[16] Our contention is that the social uses of technology should be incorporated into ICT strategies aiming to engage with politics. Advocating the use of chatrooms and message boards for political debate must be accompanied, therefore, by an awareness that these forums can pose a potential threat to young people.

Certain characteristics of the internet simultaneously enable and endanger. The anonymity of cyberspace can be empowering for people who find it hard to communicate in face-to-face situations.[17] In particular, anonymity can actively empower the vulnerable and at risk, as proven by the success of Childline. Safe in the knowledge their identity cannot be determined, young people are able to seek advice about health and personal safety over the telephone, and Childline has gone on to become one of Britain's most successful children's charities, having received over one million calls since it was launched in 1986.[18] But anonymity can also render young people vulnerable and at risk from exploitation.

However, perhaps the greatest danger of all is that the potential threat to young people is used to justify restriction of their access to the internet. Far from being an enabler of change, use of the internet could become a barrier to engagement if over-protective attitudes are allowed to restrict young people's access. The people who abuse technology are the danger, and not the technology itself. In the same way that we teach young people to protect themselves against 'stranger danger', we need to equip them with the knowledge and strategies to stay safe and 'play safe' in cyberspace.

Virtual worlds and real-time risks

The most serious risk comes from paedophiles attempting to 'groom' young people via the internet in preparation for real-life encounters. A recent survey of 10–17-year-olds in America found that almost one in five had received some kind of sexual solicitation on the internet in the previous year.[19] The 'Chat Wise Street Wise' report suggests that incidents of sex offenders meeting children online and gaining their trust are increasing both in the UK and USA.[20] In a number of high-profile cases, these virtual relationships have become actual encounters with horrifying consequences.

The number of convictions against paedophiles who target young people via the internet continues to grow, and the severity of the outcomes is also escalating.[21]

The most common threat to young people using the internet is exposure to sexually explicit, violent, racist and other offensive material. Entering the name of the popular doll Barbie into a search engine generates as many pornographic sites as it does those for Mattel's popular icon, and innocent searches can confront young people with material that they may find distressing. We consider below what can be done to reduce the frequency with which younger children encounter such material and examine the issues affecting older children who deliberately access inappropriate sites.

Tooled up

Software tools can help protect young people against inappropriate and offensive material. Most public facilities providing online access to young people use firewalls – electronic mechanisms that are triggered by certain words, activate an alarm and prevent the user from gaining access to sites containing those words. Walled gardens, an even more secure alternative, only allow young people to enter sites that have been approved and registered as suitable for access with the server.

Problems are inherent in both systems. Not only do they both compromise young people's freedom of information, but they actively limit the extent to which young people can access valuable online resources. If a word like 'sex' activates a firewall, it prevents young people from accessing many of the useful sex education sites available via the web. Firewalls are unable to differentiate between trigger words and innocuous words that happen to contain the letters of more inappropriate words. James Gardiner, Deputy Managing Director of Redbus Management, has pointed out that firewalls prevent young people from '[finding out about] Marseilles or Scunthorpe, looking up a recipe for chicken breasts or finding information about the garden bird the blue-tit'.[22] Similarly, walled gardens need to be updated regularly if they are to provide access to the most current and relevant information, and this makes them expensive to maintain. The challenge, therefore, is to balance the need for security with the right to access and to find ways of managing risk effectively.

Superhighway safety patrol

Most current evidence suggests that young people primarily use the internet for socialising with their friends, and that the majority of cyber-interactions are simply virtual extensions of actual relationships. The solution must not be to prevent young people from accessing the internet, or even restricting their use to educational purposes only; it lies in educating them to a level of internet proficiency and social development that will enable them to take responsibility for their own safety online.

This has been the aim of a number of children's organisations, such as NCH, Childnet International and Youth Org UK. They all propose a series of similar guidelines for young people, recommending that they never disclose personal details, never arrange to meet anyone they have contacted online unless they do so in a public place and accompanied by an adult, and report to an adult any material they encounter that they find offensive. There are also guidelines for parents recommending ways of monitoring young people's use of the internet in the home. There is evidence to suggest that such campaigns have been successful in raising young people's awareness of online dangers. In June 2000 around 29 per cent of young people surveyed said they would give out personal contact details over the net, but by November of the same year the figure had fallen to just 11 per cent.[23] Valuable and effective as this advice may be, it places the emphasis on deterring paedophiles, and therefore offers few solutions to the more common problem of exposure to offensive and inappropriate material.

Recent research has advocated the introduction of a new policy tool, a Surfing Proficiency Certificate, which will ensure that all children have, at minimum, a basic level of literacy and safety awareness.[24] Sonia Livingstone, who has researched young people's online freedom and safety extensively, argues:

> Empowerment depends upon literacy. If the internet offers
> opportunities to transform children's education, leisure and
> cultural participation, it is crucial that they have the skills and
> competencies to take advantage of these opportunities.[25]

The guidelines and initiatives set out above tend to apply to younger children, who are most likely to find themselves in dangerous cyber-situations inadvertently. However, among older age groups, the problem tends to be deliberate accessing of inappropriate sites. A recent survey suggests that one in five internet users under the age of 17 are deliberately accessing pornographic material.[26] Part of the internet's attrac-

tion is precisely that it is a private experience free from adult regulation and censorship, affording young people the opportunity to see and
do things that adults may not approve of. This situation therefore
creates a dilemma in which the need to promote young people's safety
on the internet must be balanced against censorship and underpinned
by a degree of trust.

Interchill deliberately chooses not to have a firewall, but all users are
asked to sign a contract stating that they will not deliberately access
offensive material and that doing so will not only result in their exclu-
sion from the facility, but may result in the closure of the unit altogether. Steve Waterhouse says:

> It's about giving [young people] responsibility, and also making
> them aware of what the consequences of breaking that responsi-
> bility will be and giving them trust within clear boundaries.[27]

Interchill also ensures that users are never online without a member
of staff present and the workstations are configured in a horseshoe
arrangement, which means the screens of the terminals can always be
seen by the supervisors. Interchill's decision not to use firewalls,
combined with its well-designed room layout and contract for users,
demonstrates that trust when combined with creative solutions
compromises neither young people's safety nor access to the internet.

The web and Whitehall

Although much can be done at grass roots level to promote the safety
of young people online, the government still has an obligation to fulfil
its pledge to make Britain the safest country in the world for young
people to access the internet.[28] The Labour government has already
implemented a series of measures, including:

- a task force on child protection on the internet, which brings
  government, internet service providers, the police and children's
  charities together to develop a strategy for improving the protection of young people on the internet

- £25 million to set up a new police National Hi-Tech Crime Unit and funding up to 80 specialist investigators to tackle all kinds of internet crime
- the Regulation of Investigatory Powers Act 2000, which gives police and other law enforcement agencies powers to intercept and decrypt communications between child pornographers.

Labour's 2001 manifesto proposed the following additional measures:

- new 'paedophile prevention orders' to protect children from paedophile approaches over the net
- a 'kitemark' scheme, which will provide parents with clear and independent advice about what they can expect from different internet service providers, by rating each one against a safety checklist and assigning a star rating
- a challenge to every company selling personal computers into the family market to preinstall high security software, so that parents can be sure their children's machines are as safe as they can be for the internet from the moment they are turned on
- working with the industry and children's charities to develop a guidance pack on safe internet use, which can be distributed with every personal computer sold.

Barriers to breakthrough

Such measures are welcome, yet in developing a cross-sector commitment to fulfil the government's pledge, a further barrier to change emerges, perpetuated by the ICT industry itself. A major obstacle in 'cleaning up' the internet is that the industry is averse to any kind of mandatory regulation. John Carr, a researcher at NCH who specialises in young people's use of technology, argues that internet service providers are extremely competitive, and most of their social policies are designed not so much for the good of internet users themselves, but to strengthen their brand image. In a recent presentation to the Council of Europe he claimed:

There seems to be a marked reluctance on the part of ISPs to share information with each other or to embrace minimum industry standards. The bigger ISPs in particular, want to be free to market themselves aggressively and compete against each other in terms of their own brands. They each provide broadly similar services, with perhaps marginal differences, but tend to use a variety of names to describe their products as part of a deliberate commercial policy to distinguish themselves from the competition.[29]

Young people are encouraged to align themselves with a particular cyber brand identity so internet service providers tend to develop their own initiatives as a way of strengthening their own brand values. Consequently, companies tend to resist industry-wide standards and common codes of practice.

Lessons learned

Although dangerous contacts and inappropriate material represent serious problems, the limitation of young people's access to the internet is also a serious threat. Both require careful management if young people's use of the internet is to be optimised.

Adults may disapprove, but the freedom that the internet gives young people is a major part of its allure, and if young people are to be encouraged to participate and engage with society through the use of technology, it is crucial that this freedom is not compromised. Preventing young people from using the internet unless supervised by an adult is not the solution. The challenge is to manage risk with responsibility by providing young people with a sufficient level of ICT literacy that will enable them to understand the risks and take responsibility for their own safety online.

It is the social, as opposed to the information-finding, applications of the net that create the most exciting and dynamic opportunities for encouraging young people to engage with political ideas, but if they are to be promoted as innovative tools for engagement, then the debate surrounding their safety cannot be neglected.

Anonymity is at the crux of this debate because, although it can lead to exploitation, it can also empower. The next chapter addresses this issue in greater detail.

Websites of interest
www.interchill.co.uk
www.nch.org.uk
www.childnet-int.org
www.youth.org.uk
www.nua.com/surveys

5. Empowerment

Although the voting age was lowered to 18 in 1969, in the 30 years that have followed Britain has failed to cultivate a culture of political empowerment for young people. As a recent report by the Carnegie Young People Initiative highlighted:

 Compared to other countries, most [British] young people do not expect their schools or local services to share power over key decisions . . . .[T]here is a need to move beyond tokenism and ensure that young people have a genuine influence over deci-sion-making. Too many consultation exercises or youth forums have little leverage over the people and institutions that count.[30]

The case studies profiled in earlier chapters have been positive examples of how consultation exercises have formed the basis for new initiatives and policy, but instances in which commitment to young people's participation manifests itself in tangible outcomes remain rare. Expectation is raised, and in some ways ICTs have exacerbated these false hopes by providing even more opportunities for surveying the opinions of young people, via email, online surveys and telephone voting on single issues. Yet in spite of the growing points of contact between young people and decision-makers, the lack of tangible outcomes continues to disappoint. It would be wrong to suggest that young people are even less included in decision-making than in the past but, as they are now consulted more, the gap between the volume and frequency of their contributions and the resulting changes that occur appears to be widening.

In January 2002, Tony Blair announced that he had recruited a new, 30-strong team of advisers comprised entirely of 11–18-year-olds. The Children and Young Persons Advisory Forum is to be consulted on issues such as education, health, transport and crime but, although welcome, the government's record in listening to the views of young people and implementing their suggestions is poor.[31]

The evidence suggests that while the government is well versed in the rhetoric of youth involvement it has problems translating this into practice.

The justification for greater political empowerment of young people is simple; they are not only future citizens, but also stakeholders in their local communities and public services, and civic society more generally. As such, they should be granted a greater input into the decisions governing them. Yet the governance of these services seldom reflects the fact that young people are a significant user group.

Young people are often fluent in the language and activities of consumer power. There is a basic level of customer service that young people come to expect as consumers and a certain amount of power they can exercise over those who produce consumable goods and services.

ICTs and the growth of consumerism give the political opinions, suggestions and ideas of young people a degree of prominence and visibility far exceeding that which they have within formal political structures. New technologies have enabled young people to raise their profile and disseminate their views on matters as trivial as who should win *Big Brother* through to websites devoted to the prevention of bullying (see the 'Lewisham Listens' case study profiled in chapter 3) and cyber-activism campaigns designed to force multinational corporations like McDonald's to look again at their company policies (see www.macspotlight.com). This increased public profile runs in tandem with the increasing desire for, and expectation of, political empowerment.

Political empowerment for young people has two distinct aspects. First, it is important to nurture interest in political ideas and debate by providing the means by which young people can develop and express their opinions. Second, young people need greater access to and influence over the formal systems of governance that make decisions affecting them. In this context, it becomes possible to define a role for ICTs. This chapter aims to show how certain characteristics of new technologies can be empowering for young people, and how well thought out initiatives could be useful tools and points of reference for decision-makers committed to young people's participation.

Powerless to change anything?

Unless the expression of political ideas is made meaningful to young people before they are eligible to vote, Britain could be faced with a major democratic deficit. Alison Park from the National Centre for Social Research has identified a potential 'lag effect': although people become more inclined to vote as they get older, there is a bigger gap between the most and least interested age groups than ever before.[32]

The citizenship curriculum, due to be taught in secondary schools from September 2002, is the outcome of a major policy designed to promote the importance of participating in civil society and endowing politics with a relevance that it appears to lack for young people at the moment. Three major strands run throughout the citizenship education programme:

- *social and moral responsibility*
  pupils learning from the very beginning, self-confidence and socially and morally responsible behaviour, both in and beyond the classroom, towards those in authority and towards each other

- *community involvement*
  pupils learning about becoming helpfully involved in the life and concerns of their neighbourhood and communities, including learning through community involvement and service to the community

- *political literacy*
  pupils learning about the institutions, problems and practices of our democracy and how to make themselves effective in the life of the nation, locally, regionally and nationally through skills and values as well as knowledge – a concept wider than political knowledge alone.[33]

Although it may ensure a basic level of political and civic literacy, this approach alone offers very little incentive for young people to engage with these agendas. If they cannot be offered any influence over the 'institutions . . . and practices of our democracy', the situation remains largely unchanged. Political ideas may well stimulate, but young people will remain 'switched off' from the people, systems, organisations and mechanisms that implement them.

Speaking up and speaking out

The right to vote, granted at age 18, entitles people to an input to the formal mechanisms of politics. Yet by that age, the possibility of engaging with a system from which they have previously been excluded does not hold much attraction for many young people.

One of the ways in which politics can be made meaningful is by encouraging young people to develop their own sense of a political identity and to speak out about issues that have a bearing on their everyday lives. The internet can be a very powerful medium through which this can be achieved, as the work of the Greater East Belfast Youth Strategy Group shows.

Greater East Belfast Youth Strategy Group and the Voices On-Line Conference
In October 1998 the Greater East Belfast Youth Strategy Group was established. Its aim was to pull together all the various organisations in and around East Belfast that were working with young people, to examine the issues affecting them and to find ways of empowering them so that they could make a greater contribution to their communities, based on a better understanding of that community.

In March 1999, the strategy group hosted a workshop entitled 'Listening to Young People: The Current and Future Policing of Northern Ireland'. Forty-two young people took part, from a mixture of Catholic and Protestant backgrounds, and met with police commissioners from the RUC. They debated a number of issues relating to policing in Belfast and the perceived prejudices of the RUC but, crucially, achieved some tangible goals, such as making changes to the police uniform so that it was seen as less intimidating.

However, Matt Milliken, youth coordinator for the Strategy Group, observed that although the participants were willing to discuss contentious issues they still strived for consensus, and were reluctant to disagree with their peers. He was also concerned about the impossibility of finding a neutral venue in a city as politically charged as Belfast. Seeing the potential of the internet for facilitating this kind of discussion, because virtual venues are politically uncontested spaces and because the anonymity of the internet offers security and confidence to those who use it to communicate, he decided to host a series of political debates online.

In June 1999 Matt Milliken organised an initiative called 'Voices On-Line'. Over the course of one day, online conferences took place in four designated, secure chatrooms, each room dealing with a 'specific theme relevant to the experience of being young and growing up in East Belfast'.[34] The themes were:

- unhealthy living
- cultural identity and self-esteem
- leisure and play facilities
- power.

The conference was open to all local young people in secondary education and early school leavers, although they were asked to agree to a participant's contract governing their conduct within the chart rooms. The debate was also moderated by a group of young people who were closely involved with the initiative. Matt Milliken estimates that a round 100 young people from East Belfast made online contributions to the debates over the course of the day.

The chatrooms enabled the participants to discuss politically sensitive issues, such as sectarianism, entirely anonymously. Catholics and Protestants were able to engage in constructive debate – an opportunity rarely encountered by young people living in East Belfast – and those with physical or learning disabilities were able to join the discussions as equals. The initiative effectively demonstrated the ability of ICTs to engage young people with political issues, but also empowered them by giving them the freedom to express opinions without censure and to engage with other young people whose political beliefs were diametrically opposed to their own in a constructive forum.

The Greater East Belfast Youth Strategy Group saw that empowerment was critical to encouraging greater participation, but that simply incorporating young people into councils and committees was not the best way to promote real engagement. The group recognised that such forums often serve adult agendas, offer little political influence to the young, and do not necessarily cultivate the strength and confidence necessary for young people to speak out about the issues that concern them. The group therefore shifted its focus towards the creation of parallel structures rather than direct involvement with adult community groups.

At the same time, the group saw that ICTs and, in particular, the internet are 'an expanding medium for communication with great potential for the promotion of the concepts of citizenship, partnership and participation'.[35] In an area as troubled as East Belfast, citizenship, partnership and participation are seen as crucial to the future.

In such a politically charged and volatile community, certain characteristics of the internet predispose it to overcoming some of the barriers to dialogue and conflict resolution. In particular, it provides a genuinely politically neutral forum for debate. There are almost no venues in East Belfast free from political associations, but Matt Milliken realised that the virtual venue of the internet offers an unparalleled degree of neutrality that would be valuable in promoting dialogue between Catholic and Protestant young people in the area. He also recognised that the anonymity of cyberspace could really give young people the confidence to speak out about political issues relevant to their own experiences without fear of censure. Matt notes:

> Bringing young people together to discuss issues of mutual concern can be difficult in [East Belfast], and when contact is established a protocol of politeness and false harmony can mask the hostility and antagonism that lies just below the surface.[36]

Aware that in face-to-face situations, young people strive for consensus and are anxious not to offend their peers, Matt felt the anonymity of the internet would give young people the confidence to voice their opinions, safe in the knowledge that their contribution was anonymous. Formulating a proposal for the Voices On-Line event, he argued that:

> Young people will be free to speak their minds within an agreed contract of behaviour and will be able to reflect before contributing their views, and without being interrupted half-

way through. Young people with disabilities will be able to contribute as equals, as will young women and young men irrespective of political or religious beliefs and aspirations. It is hoped that the safety that this neutral venue provides will promote the expression of honest and forthright views.[37]

In this particular context, the internet is also a great leveller of inequalities. In an anonymous cyber chatroom, what is said becomes the most important thing and not who said it. No contribution can be deemed any less valid than another on the basis of age, sex, race or ability, as can happen in face-to-face situations.

Over the course of the day, young people logged on to the conference to discuss a diverse range of topics, from drug-taking, leisure facilities and schools to sectarianism, national identity and power. A number of participants noted it was the first occasion they had spoken to a peer from a different religious background from their own; many more felt that using a chatroom was not only enjoyable and familiar, but conducive to interesting discussions in which genuine and valuable debate about difficult issues took place.

Voices On-Line aimed to promote dialogue rather than affect public policy. However, its success can still be measured in terms of empowerment because it not only engaged with young people on their own terms through a medium with which they are familiar, but also exploited the characteristics of that medium to encourage their confidence as citizens. The Voices On-Line debate gave all those who participated an opportunity to voice their opinions on relevant but sometimes contentious issues in an environment where they were not simply discounted or discredited on the basis of their age or any other factor that might otherwise count against them.

From participation to policy

As discussed previously, empowering young people requires more than informally nurturing their political identity. Engagement with politics requires a stronger incentive. In the East Riding of Yorkshire, the 'Say Something' website has been created as a consultation tool to find out what young people really think about the area in which they live.[38] If they complete an online survey or questionnaire, participants are entered into a draw and could win prizes such as mountain bikes or DVD players. But although this may be a powerful incentive for some young people, it offers no guarantee that any of their contributions will actually be taken into account in policy development. 'Say Something' may offer an incentive for participating but it cannot be said to be particularly empowering.

Yet just as there are characteristics of ICTs that are empowering to young people, they can also be valuable resources for decision-makers and policy architects. If young people are asked their opinion not just on the present but also on the future, policy measures could become more proactive in changing attitudes and behaviour rather than simply reacting to existing needs. One ICT initiative that has proved particularly attractive to policy-makers is Young TransNet.

Young TransNet

The Young TransNet initiative was established in 1997 as the result of a partnership between the Sainsbury's Family Charitable Trusts, the Road Danger Reduction Forum and the National Children's Bureau. The aim was to promote young people's involvement in decision-making about transport, and to make the adults who make policy decisions aware that young people not only want but also have a right to independent travel. Their age means the vast majority of schoolchildren are ineligible to drive a car, so consequently they make up a considerable proportion of those people using more sustainable forms of transport. As such, they should be given a greater say in how these services are run both now and in the future.

Originally called the Young People's Transport Information Network, the initiative sought to create educational computer software programes that would enable children and young people to explore the transport issues most relevant to them. During the three-year development phase, schools in York, Bath and the London Borough of Camden were asked to pilot a 'journey to school' survey tool and a referendum tool. Technical problems with many of the school's ICT facilities hampered the development of these tools, so eventually a decision was taken to make them available on the internet because it offers a more universal platform for providing access to the software.

Since autumn 2000, schools have been able to register to use the Young TransNet website at www.youngtransnet.org.uk. The resources on the website are free to schools and have been accredited by the National Grid for Learning in the citizenship, geography and ICT curricula. This means that pupils can complete the survey and contribute to the debate on transport issues as part of their citizenship, geography and ICT lessons. The greatest success of the site is that feedback has shown that it is proving popular with children, teachers and local highway authorities alike. The latter have been keen to get involved with the project because the website's online 'journey to school' survey provides a cost-effective way for schools to set out their plans for future travel arrangements – an initiative that the government is putting high on the agenda for local authorities to discuss with the schools under their jurisdiction.

Since April 2000, further funding has been secured for the project, enabling it to be taken on to the next stage of development. A strategy is now in place to create a series of local authority 'portals'. Bristol City, Devon, North East Lincolnshire, Oxfordshire and Somerset Councils have been involved in a pilot programme since July 2001. The portal provides local authorities with a means of drawing together data from those schools in their area that have completed surveys, but also allows them to add content to the website, such as curriculum resources, local case studies and travel plan guidance.

The Young TransNet project has developed tools that enable children and young people to contribute to the transport debate and there are already examples of how the project is having an impact on policy-makers. In Oxfordshire, Philippa Davison, a school travel plan officer, has noticed changes in approach within schools with regard to how they draw up their travel plans. Initially they were based on the responses compiled from paper questionnaires but increasingly schools are using the data collated from the responses to the Young TransNet surveys instead, because it can be compiled, collated and updated more easily.

The capacity of the website is sufficient for several online referendums to be run concurrently, and the Young TransNet project team sees this as a key factor in involving young people in decision-making. With the increasing desire of local government to engage in consultation with all their residents, including young people, and of central government commitment to the e-democracy agenda, the Young TransNet website is well placed to become a valuable resource for transport policy-makers both at local and national level.

As mentioned earlier, young people are among the biggest 'consumers' of public services, and transport is an area in which they make up a particularly significant percentage of users. More people aged between 16 and 8 use buses than any other age group, mainly because they want mobility but either cannot drive or afford to own and run a car. Many young people rely on buses to get to school and each year the government spends £500 million on home-to-school transport.[39] The 1944 Education Act provided free home-to-school transport for anyone living over three miles away from the nearest suitable school, but has since become a clear example of how policy has not adapted to changing social values. In the 60 years since the Act was passed, there has been little research into whether three miles is still a suitable distance to walk to school, given that roads have become more dangerous and consequently young people have become more vulnerable. Young TransNet aims to review the current legislative attitude towards young people and transport by using ICTs to provide up-to-date information about their transport needs both now and in the future.

The significant difference in the design of the Young TransNet survey is that it not only asks young people how they get to school but also how they would like to travel to school. The programme allows users to compare the results of different schools from different areas of the country to help build up a national picture of school transport issues, and also to view the results from a range of different perspectives.

This initiative carries an incentive for young people and adults alike. Pupils want to take part in the survey because they know the results have a genuine impact on future transport decisions taken by schools and local authorities, but decision-makers also want to use the site because it proves such a convenient and effective way of gathering information about school-related transport issues. The results from school surveys in Oxfordshire have helped to shape the County Council's 'Better Ways To School' scheme through the introduction of improved cycle and pedestrian routes. Students' participation in the project has empowered them and secured a notable degree of purchase on the people and organisations that count.

The other major achievement of the project, however, is that it has not compromised any of the other factors that appeal to young people when using ICTs as a means of participating. The website is extremely interactive. A referendum tool allows users to vote on specific transport issues, such as whether car-free zones are a good idea or not. Online discussion forums give young people the opportunity to discuss their transport choices and the effect they may have on the local and global environment; for younger children there is a game that requires them to navigate their way around the site and answer questions based on the information it contains. Young people also own much of the content. The homepage features a series of links to articles written by young people on topics from buses in Bath to cycling schemes in Slovakia. In this case, the things that make participation attractive to young people enhance the value for decision-makers of the information resource.

Lessons to be learned

Many parallels have been drawn recently between young people's enthusiasm for entertainment programmes that involve voting for people to win competitions like *Pop Idol* and voting in elections. In many ways, *Pop Idol* was uncontroversial from the point of view of its use of technology. Telephone voting is now fairly standard practice, but the speed between input and outcome clearly remains crucial to the success of the show's format. Young people voted for their favourite contestant and within an hour or so the results of the voting were made know publicly. Viewers could make a clear and almost immediate link between their vote and the next stage of the competition. As one 17-year-old from London who was interviewed for this project said:

> When I vote in *Pop Idol*, something actually happens. I liked Will so I voted for him every week and eventually he won. With politics, I'll get the chance to vote once every four years, and then I'll probably have to wait another four years to see if it actually makes any difference, and half the time I don't think it will.

Although politicians may have something to learn from the voting procedures of *Pop Idol*, in particular the strength of the link between participation and change, the show's real success was that it created a narrative and human drama that young people identified with and wanted to influence in a way that politicians seem completely incapable of. The success of *Pop Idol* was much less about the technology and much more about the way in which viewers were able to identify and build up a relationship with the contestants. Unless having an input into any system can be linked to objectives and outcomes that occur fairly frequently and can be quantified, it is unlikely that the disillusionment with formal political systems can be curbed.

ICTs have almost certainly made matters worse by providing adults with even more opportunities to canvass the opinions of young people, which raises expectations, but seldom results in young people's empowerment. The instances in which the opinions expressed by young people have had any significant impact on decision-makers and the policies they create remain few. If young people are able to develop a sense that their political views are held in the same regard as those of adults, they are likely to be more inclined to engage with the current political system more formally.

Consultation is an increasingly important stage in the decision-making process. The public, private and voluntary sectors are all being called to account for their policy decisions and need the support of their stakeholders to secure their legitimacy.

As Young TransNet has shown, it is possible to develop a consultation tool that can be accessed via the internet and is therefore available to all schools, colleges, youth centres and homes with ICT facilities. Not only does this overcome the difficulties in trying to bring together a fairly disparate group of young people to create a representative sample, but the results of surveys and questionnaires can be collated far more rapidly and updated more efficiently; this will help policy-makers build a picture of developing attitudes and patterns of behaviour.

When new technologies make it so easy for adults to gain access to the views of young people, it becomes difficult to justify not incorporating them more closely into the decision-making process. Ultimately, ICTs have a role to play in both the informal and formal process of empowering young people. At the moment, the quality of the attempts to do so is varied. If using ICTs to facilitate engagement and participation holds incentives for adults and young people alike, then these technologies should become instrumental in securing political empowerment for young people.

Websites of interest
www.eastbelfast.com
www.youngtransnet.org.uk
www.saysomething.org.uk

3 The government should establish NET:ENGAGE – a network of young people throughout the country who evaluate ICT initiatives aimed at promoting young people's engagement. The NET:ENGAGE officials should draw up their own evaluation criteria, which might include:

- the appropriateness of language, tone and content
- the use of good layout and design, including the ease of navigation through the site
- the ratio of young-people-owned content to adult-owned content
- the range and effectiveness of interactive features
- the incentives for participating
- the effectiveness of the initiative in promoting the views of young people and ensuring they are included within the decision-making agenda
- how much fun it is.

Initiatives that score highly would be rewarded with the equivalent of a 'kitemark', reflecting a strong commitment to promoting political participation through technology.

4 All government websites should include at least one page aimed specifically at young people, and a minimum 75 per cent of the content must be designed, owned and managed by young people themselves.

5 In order to achieve this, the government should run an annual, national competition inviting young people to design these webpages. Entering this competition could be included within the curricula for design technology and ICT, although it should not be limited to schools. Youth clubs and other facilities providing ICT access for young people should be encouraged to submit entries and the winning page(s) will be incorporated into the national government websites.

6 Government should extend its example of producing versions of consultation and other documents, where appropriate, designed specifically for young people. The 2002 green paper on reforming 14–19 education included a version produced specifically for 14–19-year-olds.

7 Government should also fund the creation of a citizenship portal. Designed to enhance the forthcoming citizenship curriculum, the site could be used as a teaching resource, but would also provide links to all the initiatives awarded the NET:ENGAGE kitemark. These initiatives should be accredited within the curricula to which they are most relevant – citizenship, ICT, and so on – so that students could participate in the initiatives as part of their study programme.

8 The extent to which young people have used ICT to engage with politics, decision-making and civic society should be reflected in the National Record of Achievement. The National Curriculum guidance on citizenship and ICT should be reviewed to include effective engagement in public and community decision-making using ICTs.

9 The Connexions Smartcard (due to be launched by the government shortly) should be used to reward young people who use ICTs as a means of political engagement. Having logged on to an accredited website, users would be prompted to enter their Connexions Smartcard identification number. Having contributed to the initiative (for instance, by taking part in an online debate, voting in a straw poll, completing an online survey or posting a message) they would receive a certain number of 'participation points'. Accumulated points could later be redeemed against a variety of services (such as entry to leisure and sports facilities or cinemas) or products (such as CDs, computer games or mobile phone top-up cards).

10 The location of free ICT facilities should be reviewed and refined to reflect the kinds of environments that young people like and

spend significant amounts of time in. This might involve giving young people free access to technology in cinemas, shopping malls, leisure centres and youth shelters.

In the medium term

1 The implications of the young people's e-democracy agenda for third generation mobile technology needs to be investigated more fully by government and the industry, in conversation with young people.

2 The popularity of text messaging and telephone voting (made popular by programmes such as *Big Brother* and *Pop Idol*) could be harnessed to political effect. Given young people's interest in single-issue politics, mobile phones could be used to vote in referendums on key issues of the day, providing certain outcomes could be guaranteed as a result.

3 Similarly, government and the relevant industries need to consider the role that digital and interactive television might play in supporting greater youth participation in the e-democracy agenda.

4 The computer industry must invest in the development of more sophisticated firewalls and walled gardens which are able to distinguish between sites that are unsuitable or inappropriate for young people and those that are valuable educational resources. This might involve registering all pornographic or potentially offensive sites with a URL that indicates the nature of the content, for example, with the suffix '.adult'. A wider debate about public risk, youth, parental and community responsibility needs to be launched in order to increase awareness of the issues and develop a more robust consensus on the need for appropriate safeguards and balance.

5 The Audit Commission should review the effectiveness of local authority arrangements for consulting and involving young people in local democracy and programmes to improve service quality and delivery.

6 Central and local government should investigate ways in which lessons for practice and policy in youth engagement can be learned from other countries with a strong record in engaging young people and link such lessons to NET:ENGAGE and the citizenship portal.

If implemented, these suggestions would not only enable young people to engage with politicians and decision-makers more effectively, but would also enable adults to relate to young people better and on their own terms. Technology can increase the number of points of contact between a young citizen and political institutions. With such multiple inputs, those in authority will eventually have to share control over the outputs more widely. The result, far from undermining formal politics and governance, should endow it with a meaning and relevance that it appears to lack for young and old alike.

If the outcome of implementing these proposals is a more engaging, participatory and responsive political system, in which interest in politics and civic society can be cultivated early and sustained for life, then the implications for the future of democracy can only be positive.

Notes

1 A Dowty and A Bonsu, 'Idle journalists, idle pens?', *Observer*, 20 Jan 2002

2 Source: The National Centre for Social Research

3 Source: Charter 88

4 *Election 2001: the official results* (Politicos and the Electoral Commission, 2001)

5 Only 38 per cent of 18–25-year-olds used their vote, Source: www.mori.co.uk/about/news/ash.htm

6 T Bentley, *It's Democracy Stupid* (Demos: 2001)

7 Source: All statistics are taken from the official Millennium Volunteers website at www.millenniumvolunteers.gov.uk

8 The term was first coined in the US, but is developed as a concept by Daniel Stedman Jones with Ben Crowe in *Transformation Not Automation* (Demos, 2001)

9 Source: www.jupitermmxi.com/xp/uk/home.xml

10 Source: *Closing the Digital Divide: information and communication technologies in deprived areas*, a report by Policy Action Team, DTI, 15 February 2000

11 Ibid

12 Ibid

13 The National Curriculum for ICT (DfES, 2002)

14 Ibid

15 Ibid

16 Source: www.silicon.com

17 The work of the Greater East Belfast Youth Strategy Group, profiled as a case study in chapter 5, is a good example

18 See: www.childline.org.uk

19 'Online Victimisation: a report on the nation's youth', http://jama.amassn.org/issues/v285n23/abs/jbr10028.html

20 Sonia Livingstone, *Online Freedom and Safety for Children*, IPPR/Citizens Online Research Publication No 3. Nov 2001

21 In America, several young people have been murdered by people they initially contacted via the internet.

22 S Brooke, 'Porn risk to children awaits solution', www.telegraph.co.uk

23 Source: www.nua.com/surveys

24 Sonia Livingstone, *Online Freedom and Safety for Children*, IPPR/Citizens Online Research Publication No 3. Nov 2001

25 Ibid

26 Source: NUA internet surveys at www.nua.com/surveys

27 Quoted in an interview with Steve Waterhouse from Interchill, 7 November 2001

28 Pledge made by Jack Straw (then Home Secretary) on 20 May 2001

29 J Carr, 'User Power and Media Competence: Combining protection and education', a paper presented to the Council of Europe, Strasbourg, November 2001

30 R Gurumurthy in foreword to D Cutler and R Frost, *Taking the Initiative: Promoting young people's involvement in public decision making in the UK* (The Carnegie United Kingdom Trust, 2001)

31 Alexander Dowty (aged 13) and Akosua Bonsu (aged 15) 'Idle journalists, idle pens?', *Observer*, 20 Jan 2002

32 A Park, 'The Generation Game', in British Social Attitudes, 17th report, 2000–2001 (Sage, 2001)

33 Source: www.dfes.gov.uk/citizenship/teac_stra.cfm

34 M Milliken, 'Voices @ Chatnet', report from the Voices On-Line conference, June 1999

35 Ibid

36 Ibid

37 Ibid

The Bride of
the Delta
Queen

The Bride of
the Delta
Queen

Janet Dailey

OPEN ROAD

INTEGRATED MEDIA

NEW YORK

ISBN 978-1-4976-3962-1

This edition published in 2014 by Open Road Integrated Media, Inc.
345 Hudson Street
New York, NY 10014
www.openroadmedia.com

Introduction

I ntroducing Janet Dailey's AMERICANA. Every novel in this collection is your passport to a romantic tour of the United States through time-honored favorites by America's First Lady of romance fiction. Each of the fifty novels is set in a different state, researched by Janet and her husband, Bill. For the Daileys it was an odyssey of discovery. For you, it's the journey of a lifetime.

Preface

When I first started writing back in the Seventies, my husband Bill and I were retired and traveling all over the States with our home—a 34' travel trailer—in tow. That's when Bill came up with the great idea of my writing a romance novel set in each one of our fifty states. It was an idea I ultimately accomplished before switching to mainstream fiction and hitting all the international bestseller lists.

As we were preparing to reissue these early titles, I initially planned to update them all—modernize them, so to speak, and bring them into the new high-tech age. Then I realized I couldn't do that successfully any more than I could take a dress from the Seventies and redesign it into one that would look as if it were made yesterday. That's when I saw that the true charm of these novels is their look back on another time and another age. Over the years, they have become historical novels, however recent the history. When you read them yourself, I know you will feel the same.

So, enjoy, and happy reading to all!

The Bride of the Delta Queen

1

Her fingers curled around the post supporting the balcony overhead. Green flecks sparkled in her hazel eyes as she surveyed the
narrow, bricked street. This was it—Vieux Carré, the French
Quarter of New Orleans with its brick buildings decorated with
ornate Spanish grillwork making balconies of iron lace.

After almost two full days of sight-seeing, Selena Merrick still hadn't
become accustomed to the wonder of it. She had planned this vacation for
years, it seemed. Not that everything had gone according to her plan. Her
best friend, Robin Michels, was to have come along but had to cancel her
reservations at the last minute owing to a family crisis.

It had never crossed Selena's mind to cancel the trip or postpone it because
of Robin. As she looked down the picturesque streets, a faint smile curved her
lips. Selfishly she was glad she had come alone. She could tour the Quarter at
her own pace, see as much or as little as she wanted without consulting the
wishes of anyone else. And there were times when Robin, good friend or not,
could be a soppingly wet blanket.

On the opposite side of the street, a white lace balcony caught the rays of
the setting sun, the white ironwork reflecting the gold tint. This silent

1

reminder of passing time prodded Selena into movement. Threading her way through the stream of fellow tourists, she crossed the street and directed her footsteps toward her hotel.

The sunlight warmed her shoulders, bared by the halter sundress in a springlike apricot print. The closeness of the air, heavy with humidity, made Selena think of summer instead of the last week of April. It tightened the natural wave of her light auburn hair and made her skin feel sticky with moisture. She would definitely need to shower before changing for dinner.

A sidewalk café bar added to the congestion of pedestrian traffic on the narrow sidewalk. A passerby accidentally jostled Selena, knocking her sideways into one of the wrought-iron chairs and its occupant.

"Sorry," Selena said, offering a quick, smiling apology to the man she had bumped.

A glancing look caught the movement of crisp black hair as the man nodded his head in acceptance of her apology. The incident forced Selena to change her path, skirting the edge of the tables that intruded out onto the sidewalk.

Selena paid no attention to the men grouped around the next table. Their loud talk and raucous laughter blended in with the street sounds. But she had not escaped their notice, with her gleaming bare shoulders and copper hair.

As she drew level with their table, one of the men rose and staggered into her path, checking her steps. Selena smiled briefly in apology, unaware that he had deliberately blocked her way, and paused to wait for a break in the steady stream of tourists to walk around the man.

"Why don't you join us for a drink, Red?" The man's voice was slurred, indicating the he had already indulged in more than he could hold.

Startled only momentarily, Selena cast a sweeping look over the group of men, noting the conventioneers' badges on the pockets of their jackets. Amusement flickered in her eyes. They were undoubtedly respectable businessmen who, in their own home towns, would not be caught dead inviting a strange girl to drink with them in a place as public as this café bar.

"Thanks, but no," she refused, unable to take offense at their invitation.

An empty chair was being offered to her. "Come on, honey, sit down with us," another voice spoke up.

"Thank you, boys. It's really nice of you to offer, but—" Selena refused again with an eloquent shrug, the sparkle of laughter remaining in her eyes.

"Aw, come on, Red," the first man cajoled. "Have a drink with us and later I'll buy you dinner," he promised with an expansive sweep of his hand.

Still smiling, Selena shook her head. She found no threat in the situation. It was broad daylight and the streets and sidewalks were crowded with peo-

2

ple. She had opened her mouth to refuse again when the first man bent his head toward her in an attitude that suggested secrecy. But he didn't lower the volume of his voice.

"You can call a couple of your friends for the guys and we'll really do up the town."

At first, Selena was astonished. "My friends?" she echoed, before suddenly realizing that they thought she was a native of New Orleans instead of a tourist like themselves.

"You know," a third voice chimed in to prompt her, his sotto voice ringing loudly for all to hear. "Your cohorts, other ladies of the evening like yourself. I like blondes," he proclaimed.

Selena nearly choked on a bubble of laughter. Try as she would, she found the situation much too funny to feel insulted or degraded. Simultaneously she also realized that they wouldn't believe her if she denied her alleged profession. To assert her valid claim that she was a minister's daughter would only add to their romantic image of what a fallen woman should be.

Assessing the group of men eagerly awaiting her reply, she couldn't help thinking that they were overgrown little boys. They were all dressed in the best suits and ties, good material and well tailored, but none of the suits was expensive—a fact she could attest to, thanks to her eye for clothes and four years of experience as inventory clerk and part-time buyer for an exclusive department store in Des Moines. She had often railed at the job since the only reason she had ever been promoted was because other employees had left, but now she was glad of her experience.

"Sorry, boys." Laughter riddled her voice despite her attempts to restrain it. There seemed to be one safe way out, and Selena intended to take it, seeing only harmless fun in choosing pretense. "No offense intended, but I don't think you could afford me."

Her response set them back in their chairs, except for the one who was standing beside her. His expression was wreathed in curious awe.

"How much?" he whispered, holding his breath.

Selena named the first sum that came to her mind in an answering whisper. The man's mouth opened and closed several times, and Selena's lips twitched in an effort to control her laughter at the whole ludicrous situation.

"Goodbye, boys," she beamed.

As she half turned to slip into the throng of tourists, her attention was caught by a pair of dark eyes assessing her with sweeping coolness. They belonged to the man seated alone at the next table, the one she had accidentally bumped into. Selena recognized the ebony black hair growing so crisply, and there was something speculative in the arch of his eyebrow. It seemed to be mocking and interested, in an amused sort of way.

3

Unfortunately, as far as Selena was concerned, her dumbstruck friend chose that moment to recover his voice and answering the whispered question of, "How much?" from his friends, he breathed, "Five hundred!"

And the dark eyebrow lifted a fraction of an inch higher. Selena's stomach muscles constricted. A slowly spreading warmth started to fire her skin as she escaped into the concealing stream of pedestrians. It had seemed harmless fun to pretend to be the shady lady of the evening the elderly gentlemen had been seeking, but Selena discovered that she didn't care to have the dark-haired man see her in that light.

Within a couple of blocks, she arrived at her hotel. In the interim, she had managed to shake the disturbing sensation as she stored up the incident in her memory, a tale to tell her friends when she returned from the vacation. It smacked of naughty adventure while being amusing at the same time.

But it also caused her to pause in front of the vanity mirror in her hotel room as she tried to discover what there was about her that would have led those respectable and elderly gentlemen to believe that she was a member of that old profession.

Was it the shimmering copper color of her hair, she wondered curiously. Red, the color for a scarlet woman? Between the humidity—which increased her hair's tendency to wave—and the occasional breeze that had sneaked down the narrow streets, her shoulder-length style was in charming disarray.

Sighing, Selena dismissed the color of her hair as the cause. Perhaps it was the bold gleam in her green-flecked eyes, but it had always been there, shining through long, sun-kissed lashes.

Her father, the Reverend Andrew James Merrick, had often accused her of embracing life too passionately. Of course, he never meant it in the lustful sense of the word. He was referring to her lack of fear; Selena's inclination to rush in where angels would fear to tread.

Strangely enough, this inclination had never been true when it came to relationships with the opposite sex. With projects and friends, yes—Selena would tackle anything and anyone if it was for the benefit of someone else—but when it came to her own emotions and feelings, she was very cautious.

There was nothing outstanding about the rest of her features, just the usual forehead, nose, cheeks, jaw and chin that are required to make a face complete. Maybe it was her lips, she considered. A friend had once described them as full and sensuous, but she hadn't paid too much attention to the remark. Looking at them now, shining with gloss, Selena admitted without conceit that her mouth was nicely shaped and possibly inviting.

But she was no nearer to discovering what it had been that had prompted the gentlemen to make such a mistake. Shaking her head in bewilderment, she

4

took a step away from the mirror. That was when she saw it—the composite picture of herself.

Wholesome beauty met with the boldness of her eyes, the sensuous lines of her lips and the attracting brightness of her hair. It was nothing blatant, Selena realized. Probably it could be discovered in any attractive woman if that was what a man was looking for. It was a case of seeing what a person wanted to see.

It was almost a relief to discover there was nothing abandoned or wanton about her looks. Striking, yes—attractive, yes—and a well-rounded figure, too, but nothing licentious.

Laughing at herself, Selena turned away from the mirror and began untying the halter straps of her sundress. Robin would have been appalled at the reason Selena had so minutely dissected her appearance. As far as that went, Selena smiled to herself, her girl friend would have been appalled at the incident.

No, she corrected, Robin would have been indignantly outraged by the mistake and would never have dreamed of perpetuating the impression, even in good fun. Selena decided maybe it was just as well that Robin hadn't been able to come along on the trip. She was probably going to have more fun without her.

Later, as she finished dressing for dinner, she retracted the last thought. It would have been more fun if Robin was along. No matter how liberated the times were supposed to be, it still raised eyebrows when a woman went to a bar or a nightclub alone. As it was, Selena knew she would draw a lot of curious glances sitting alone in the restaurant.

New Orleans was a city renowned for its nighttime entertainment. Judging by some of the posters and advertisements Selena had seen on the famed Bourbon Street, there were some clubs that she wasn't interested in but there were other, reputable night spots that she would have liked to experience.

With her hair secured in a sophisticated pleat, Selena smoothed the sides absently with her fingertips and reached for the tricorner shawl that matched the flame-orange dress she wore. It was an unusual shade and one that oddly accented and complemented the fiery lights in her hair. She draped the shawl around her shoulders and tied the ends in a loose knot.

Stepping out her door into the carpeted hotel hallway, she paused to make certain the room key was in her evening purse, then closed the door. She had barely taken two steps from her door when a door farther down the hallway opened and a man stepped out.

It took Selena about as long to recognize where she had seen him before as it took him to remember her. It was the man she had bumped into before encountering the older group of men.

Her first sinking thought was—why had she chosen such a brilliantly colored dress to wear? Why hadn't she picked something from her wardrobe that was more demure and unobtrusive? Fighting the urge to scurry back into her room, Selena continued down the hallway. Her steps had slowed as she crossed her fingers, hoping he would ignore her and continue on his way.

Of course, he didn't. He stood waiting expectantly for her, those glinting dark eyes sweeping her from head to toe. The look branded her with the iron Selena herself had put in the fire.

"Hello, Red." His voice was huskily pitched, carrying that note of amused interest.

It seemed pointless to ignore him or pretend that she didn't recognize him. Selena was positive that she had already made him aware of her recognition. *What a fine mess I've got myself into this time,* she thought.

"Hello," she returned the greeting accompanied by what she hoped was a detached and disinterested smile.

Slipping his room key in his suit pocket, he stepped forward to meet her. Selena couldn't make up her mind whether she should walk past him or stop.

Her fleeting glimpse of him at the café had not prepared her for his bulk. Several inches taller than her five-foot-six frame, the man was huskily built. He was wearing a light tan suit, the jacket unbuttoned to reveal a matching vest. Selena didn't need to see the lining to know it had been hand-tailored to fit his muscular frame. The richly textured fabric cried "money," as did the assurance in his craggy male features.

"Are you coming or going?" he inquired, meeting her boldly inspecting stare and returning it with a mirthless quirk to his mouth.

In the glinting blackness of his eyes, Selena saw what he had left unsaid in his question. The very fact that they had met a second time in the hall-way of the hotel indicated that she must have come from one of the rooms. And in that silently suggestive look of his, he was considering what had gone on in that room.

Her anger boiled near the surface, but Selena determinedly cooled it. She had no one to blame but herself for what he was thinking.

At some point in his approach, she had stopped. It was a mistake, she realized, and one not so easily rectified, since the breadth of his shoulders blocked her way.

"Going," she answered his question and made an attempt to pass him, hoping he would move out of her path.

He didn't budge an inch. "Where?"

Her father had often told her that the truth could never hurt. Selena hoped he was right as she answered frankly, "To dinner."

Unknowingly she was clutching her purse, knuckles white with the tense-ness of her grip. His gaze slid to her hand, drawing her attention to her death hold on her evening bag. She guessed what construction he placed on that—

6

that she was protecting her monetary payment for services rendered. She seethed with frustration.

"Did you work up an appetite?" The question was almost a taunt.

This time Selena didn't attempt to contain her anger, letting it blaze in her eyes. "I find that remark crude, sir. Excuse me." And started to push her way past him, all stiff and proud.

His large hand rested on the bareness of her arm to stop her. "That was crude," he acknowledged smoothly. "I had no business saying it to a lady of your caliber. I'm sorry."

"Of your caliber." The words taunted her. If he had just left it with the word "lady," Selena might have been more willing to accept his apology.

Instead all she could manage was a freezing, "That's quite all right," that made a lie of her acceptance,

His dark gaze scanned her features, his own expression inscrutable. "Will you be dining alone?"

He was making no attempt to hold her, but Selena found she couldn't move or pull her arm from the light touch of his sun-browned hand. Yet her muscles were rigidly resisting his nearness.

"Perhaps," she answered noncommittally.

He interpreted her reply to mean she was dining alone. "As luck would have it, I'm without a dinner companion myself tonight." His right hand was thrust in his trouser pocket, holding his jacket open with studied casualness. "Would you join me?"

Moments before leaving her room Selena had wished for a table companion to share her meal, but she knew instinctively that the company this man would supply would be dangerously stimulating. It was there in his shuttered dark eyes that glinted with mockery yet never revealed what he was thinking.

"No, thank you." Her rejection was coolly abrupt.

It piqued his interest even as it deepened the dimpling grooves next to his mouth. "Why not?"

"Because I choose who I dine with," Selena retorted, wishing she could bring an end to this ridiculous meeting. Why wouldn't he let her pass?

"Just as you choose who you go to bed with?" he countered in a low mocking taunt.

"Exactly!" The word burst from her in an explosion of temper.

In the back of her mind, she had been wondering how she could convince him that she had gone along with the elderly group for a harmless joke. But a red flash of anger made her feel that she owed him no explanation at all.

Something cynical flickered across his expression as one corner of his mouth slanted without humor. "I'm well aware there's a price for your time, Red. I'm prepared to pay it."

7

His right hand was withdrawn from his trouser pocket. A freezing burn seemed to hold Selena motionless as he reached out to tuck folded bills into her cleavage. At the brush of his fingers against her bare skin as his hand withdrew, the spell of immobility was broken.

Bending her head, she looked down at the green bills, aware of a distant sensation of degradation. Slowly she removed the money and lifted her gaze to his. Still no words of denunciation left her lips.

"I'm surprised," she heard herself say evenly. "You didn't strike me as the type who would have to pay for his pleasure."

He cocked his head slightly, his dark gaze sweeping over her. "Maybe I'm curious what 'pleasure' you have to offer that would be worth so much," he countered.

Something in his tone or his look, or maybe it was the sheer magnetism of his presence, warned Selena of the dangerous game she was playing. Her pulse accelerated in alarm.

"I don't happen to be selling right now," she rushed, and tried to force the money into his hand while pushing her way by him.

His hand closed around the fingers holding his money at the same moment that he took hold of her elbow. "This isn't the place for a discussion."

He was propelling her stilted legs forward. Selena's initial reaction was that he was going to force his company on her at the dinner table by directing her down the hallway to the lobby and restaurant. Her mouth was open to protest, her widened and slightly angry gaze on his strong face when he paused to reach in front of her. Her gaze swung forward as he opened a hotel room door, obviously his.

"This will be more private," he announced with a lazy, mocking glint in his eye.

Panic screamed through her nerve ends. "No, listen, please!" But she was already through the door and it had closed behind her.

She pivoted, ready to bolt out the door, but he was there, blocking her escape and regarding her pale complexion with curious bemusement. She could feel her heart thumping against her ribs.

"I think we can make a satisfactory arrangement, don't you?" he questioned, his voice smooth and husky, his expression experienced.

"Look," Selena took a shaky breath and swallowed, "this is all a mistake—"

The folded bills were still in her hand. He took them from her clenched fingers, then removed her evening bag from her other hand. Fear strangled the protest in her throat as she watched him unsnap the purse and slip the money inside.

"My purse!" she squeaked when he gave it a toss to some point behind her.

She started to turn but managed only a glance over her shoulder, enough to see her evening bag slide to a stop on top of a low dresser. The strong hands closing around the bare flesh of her upper arms kept her from turning around completely to retrieve it.

8

"It will be perfectly safe there," he assured her.

But she wasn't perfectly safe. The fact was driven sharply home to her as she felt his hands slide to the shawl, freeing the ends from the loose knot with the simplest of tugs. She clutched at the trailing ends, but they escaped her grasp as he let the shawl fall to the floor.

Selena would have stooped to pick it up, but his hands were on her arms, drawing her to his chest. Hunching her shoulders, she used her forearms to wedge a small space between them. His chest was like a solid wall, immovable.

"Don't!" she struggled.

His cheek and jaw were near her temple, the clean, spice-scented fragrance of his after-shave lotion assailing her nose. His fingers were spread across the bareness of her spine, pressing her ever closer.

"Stop acting." His breath stirred the hair near her ear as he spoke.

"I'm not acting!" Selena flared, breathing in sharply when he began nuzzling the sensitive area of her neck below her earlobe. "Did it ever occur to you that the lady might not be willing?" she gasped, twisting her head toward her shoulder to stop his exploring mouth.

He merely laughed. "It's your profession to be willing."

"Well, I'm—" Her indignant protest was lost as she made the mistake of lifting her head to deliver the protest to his face. Immediately his mouth muffled the rest of her words.

Startled, for several seconds Selena was passive under the mobile pressure of his male lips. There was a quality of arrogant mastery to his kiss, commanding rather than bruising. It was this assertion of rights that she rebelled against rather than feeling repulsed by his kiss. That, coupled with fear. She wrenched her head away from his mouth, drawing back, the storm of anger flashing green in her eyes.

A dark brow was raised in cynical mockery of her action. She was conscious of the large hand at the base of her spine, pressing her hips and legs to his taut-muscled and long-bodied frame. Fiery lights glittered behind the thick screen of his lashes, amused and passionate and confident.

"Will you let me go?" she blazed in a temper born of desperation.

She pressed her hands against his shoulder bones and strained with all her might to break out of the steel trap of his embrace. All she succeeded in accomplishing was to arch the lower half of her body more fully against his.

Impatience hardened the firm set of his mouth. "Look, this game of hard-to-get might work with your older clients, but it doesn't impress me," he stated.

Her chin and jaw were captured by long fingers to hold her mouth still for his possession. Selena was helpless to prevent it, unable to move her head, and her hand and arms were pinned between the crush of their bodies.

Soon the long, drugging kiss began to make its effects known to Selena. Like a narcotic, it weakened and relaxed her rigid muscles, and for a moment she allowed his roaming hands to mold her pliant flesh to his male form. The sensation of the kiss was threatening to become addictive.

When the fingers on her chin relaxed their hold, it took all of her willpower to slide her lips free of his kiss. He permitted it, tipping her head back in order to explore the smooth column of her neck and the hollow of her throat.

The nibbling caresses aided the drugging, and molten warmth spread through her limbs. But Selena's senses were not totally numbed. She heard the zipper of her dress being released and felt the coolness of air against her skin. At the tug on the fragile straps of her dress, she knew she was lost unless she did something quickly.

She had tested his strength and knew she was no match for it. As long as he remained the aggressor she had no hope. Her only chance was to turn the tables.

Taking a deep breath for courage, she was filled with a strange combination of fear and exhilaration. His hand was on her shoulder now, pushing away one of the offending straps, her dress hanging loosely about her.

"If you tear the dress, it will be extra," she warned on a bold and breathless note.

For a split second, he didn't move, his mouth pressed against the curve of her neck. Selena was so scared she was afraid to breathe. Thick jet-black hair brushed her jaw as he lifted his head, a complacent curve to his mouth.

There was space between them now, but his hands were still resting on her shoulders. Selena attempted an alluring, if tremulous, smile and raised sweeping eyelashes to look at him. Gently and carefully, he slipped the spaghetti straps from her shoulder and the flame-orange dress fell around her ankles.

Her lashes fluttered once, but it was the only outward sign she gave of embarrassment. Inwardly she knew her knees were threatening to buckle, and it took all her nerve not to cover the scanty lace of her strapless bra with her hands. Luckily a matching half-slip of lace kept the rest of her well covered.

Keeping the smile painted on her lips, she reached out for his hand. The smallness of her hand was soon lost in the largeness of his.

She stepped out of the dress, which lay around her ankles and unfortunately stepped out of one of her shoes, too.

She kicked the other one off as she led him farther into the room and away from the door. She stopped short of the bed, a fact the fathomless black eyes made note of while continuing to watch her with burning brightness.

Releasing his hand, she reached for his jacket, sliding a hand along the lapel. "Shall I help you off with your clothes?" The huskiness of her voice was due mainly to the fear of the moment.

A dark brow briefly flickered upward. "I think I can manage," he assured her. Shrugging, she turned away, relief washing through her with the force of a tidal wave. But he was still watching her as he peeled off his jacket and began unbuttoning his vest. Selena wandered to the mirror, patting the escaping tendrils of copper hair back into place and keeping him in view via the mirror.

After the vest came the white shirt. Selena quivered at the sight of all that naked muscle. Without an ounce of spare flesh on his torso, sunbrowned to a teak shade. All that male virility oozing from him was not a sensation to settle her already taut nerves.

When he unfastened his trousers and stepped out of one leg, she bolted. There wasn't time to worry about shoes or her red dress lying on the floor. She made a sweeping grab to retrieve her purse and darted to the door, ignoring his muffled curse.

For the first time in this misadventure, Selena felt luck was on her side. There was no one in the hallway, no one to see her racing to her hotel room in her lacy underwear. She wasted a precious second fumbling for the room key in her purse, inserted it quickly in the lock and turned it.

Opening the door and slipping into her room, she darted one last glance down the hall just as he appeared, bare chested and fastening his trousers. He looked toward the lobby instead of in Selena's direction and she quickly and silently closed the door.

Her knees buckled and she leaned weakly against the door, taking deep, quaking breaths. Sounds that were somewhere between laughter and sobs came from her throat. She sobered quickly into silence when she heard footsteps in the hall, but they gradually receded.

Gathering strength, she walked into the room to take the cotton robe from the foot of the bed and wrapped it around her. The red orange dress had been one of her favorites. It was gone for good now. Selena doubted that she would have worn it again even if she could have managed to bring it with her out of the room.

Her stomach growled, reminding her that she still hadn't had dinner. She shook her head, knowing there was no way she was going to risk bumping into that man again. Selena walked to the telephone and dialed room service.

2

Determined not to be a prisoner in her room, Selena slipped out of the hotel early the next morning. She took precautions to keep from being readily recognized, by donning dark, owl-shaped sunglasses and wearing a floppy-brimmed straw sunhat to cover her auburn hair piled beneath it.

Her fear of meeting the man a third time vanished when she stepped outside the hotel into the sunlight of a spring Sunday. Indeed, she felt like both—spring and Sunday—in her pristine white skirt and silk blouse of lime green with large white polka dots, a matching scarf and the same material tied around the hatband.

There was no hesitation in her footsteps as she left the hotel entrance. She knew exactly where she was going—to the French market to breakfast on *beignets* and chickory coffee. The route she chose was not the most direct, but Selena decided it would be picturesque, although she doubted that there was any place in the French Quarter that was not picturesque.

The French Quarter—wandering down a narrow street, Selena wondered again at the misnomer because all the architecture was decidedly Spanish. But of course, she conceded that the name was really derived because of the

French who lived in this section of New Orleans, especially when the Americans took over and attempted to anglicize the city. Selena doubted if they had ever succeeded completely.

Emerging from the shaded coolness of Pirates' Alley, she paused near the entrance of St. Louis Cathedral and marveled again at the fairy-tale turrets and steeples of its building, the oldest cathedral in the United States.

As she crossed the street, she noticed the artists setting up their wares outside the iron fences surrounding Jackson Square and promised herself she would browse through them after she had breakfast.

She took the shortcut through the square to the French market and quickly discovered that she wasn't the only one who had decided to breakfast early. The café was filled with the aroma of fresh doughnuts and *beignets*, and hungry customers, and Selena felt her appetite increasing as she sought and found an empty table and chair.

The square-shaped doughnuts, minus the hole and covered in powdered sugar, were still warm when they were served. She took a wake-up sip of the black coffee and immediately added a liberal amount of cream to weaken its potency. Chickory coffee was an acquired taste, she decided.

Later, wiping the floury sugar from her lips and hands, she hoped she had rid herself of all the powdery sweet. The coffee, she had discovered after finishing the cup, was really more palatable than she had first believed, and she accepted the refill the waiter offered.

A young boy at a nearby table grabbed his mother's arm and exclaimed excitedly, "I just heard a man say the *Delta Queen* is in! Can we go look at her?"

The mother's reply was too low for Selena to understand, but the nod of her head and the boy's hoot of joy convinced her that it had been in the affirmative. As she watched the family leave the café, the name *Delta Queen* kept running through her mind, but she couldn't remember why it should be so familiar.

The question nagged her until she finally stopped the waiter to ask him, "I heard someone say the *Delta Queen* was in. Is that a ship?"

"It's a riverboat, ma'am," he answered. "An old-time paddle wheeler, one of the last on the river that carries overnight passengers."

The pieces began to fall into place. "It's the boat that was almost forced out of service a few years ago because it was made of wood, isn't it?"

"Her superstructure is made of wood, but she has a steel hull," he corrected, "Congress has granted her a temporary exemption to keep her on the river." One corner of his mouth lifted in a half smile. "A stay of execution, you might call it."

Selena remembered the publicity that had surrounded it and her lips echoed his faint smile. "Where is she docked?"

13

The waiter hesitated, then answered, "At the Poydras Street wharf, I imagine. Do you know where that is?" Selena shook her head in regretful acknowledgment that she didn't. "It's on the other side of Canal Street, near where the International Trade Mart is."

"I know where that is," Selena nodded. "Thank you."

She knew generally where the boat was docked. With the towering trade center building in sight, it was easy to walk to it. Once there, she had to ask for more specific directions to the wharf. Reaching the wharf buildings, she stopped at the parking garage to ask again.

"The *Delta Queen?* She'll be tied up by the excursion boats," a security guard informed her. "You can walk through the garage, if you like, then turn right."

A sudden breeze tugged at her floppy hat brim as she walked on to the concrete walkway running the length of wharf buildings on the riverside. Holding onto the brim, Selena turned right, moving past the silver-painted monolith called The Admiral.

Farther down the dock, she could see a stirring of activity and walked toward it. Her view of the *Delta Queen* was blocked by other boats until she was almost upon it. At the first glimpse of the name painted on the black hull, she slowed her steps, letting her gaze run up the four-storied lady of the river.

Deckhands were moving around the forward deck, while uniformed porters carried luggage off the boat, followed by strolling, unhurried passengers. A few other spectators had gathered along the dock, some to meet disembarking passengers while others, like the family Selena had seen in the café, were simply there to see the *Delta Queen.*

At the head of a gangplank, a sign was posted that read Sorry, No Visitors At This Time, and Selena experienced a feeling of regret as she walked toward the stern. The polished teak handrails circling the top three decks and the black smokestack with its gold crown perched behind the pilothouse made her wish she could explore the interior. At the stern the red paddle wheel rested, not required to churn muddy water until the boat again left port.

One of the crew—judging by the curved figure Selena realized it was a female—was repainting the *Delta Queen's* name on the large signboard above the paddle wheel. The gold whistles of the calliope gleamed in the morning sunlight.

Here and there, Selena caught glimpses of the boat's age, most of them artfully concealed with a fresh coat of paint, reminders that the legendary *Delta Queen* was the grand old lady of the riverboats.

"Like something out of the past, isn't it?" a voice said.

Startled, Selena turned, becoming aware only at that moment of the older woman standing near her. "Yes, it is," she agreed, recovering quickly to smile. "Somehow I never realized it was such a large ship."

14

"Boat," the woman corrected gently. "Any vessel that plies the river is a boat, no matter what her size."

"A large boat, then," Selena conceded, her smile widening.

"Yes," the woman nodded. "She'll accommodate one hundred and ninety-odd passengers and a crew of seventy-five," she added in a knowledgeable tone.

"You know a lot about the *Delta Queen*, don't you?" Selena commented running a considering eye over the woman.

Almost as tall as Selena, the woman had dark hair except for a pair of silvered wings at the temples that gave her a distinguished air. There was a suggestion of crow's feet at the corners of her brown eyes, but otherwise her facial skin was relatively unlined. Selena guessed that the youthfulness of the woman's features was due to the strong bone structure of her face, because she was certain the woman was in her late fifties or very early sixties.

Although the woman was large boned, she was trim and neat in her blue summer suit. The simple lines of the tailored outfit bespoke class and the woman wore it with the ease of one accustomed to wearing good clothes. Selena suspected that the woman had never been a beauty, even in her youth, but she decided that she had probably been attractive in the same strong sort of way that she was now.

"I am very familiar with the boat and her history," the woman answered.

"You're from New Orleans?" Selena was positive that there was something in the picture the woman was presenting that she wasn't seeing.

"Yes," was the brief reply and then the woman's brown gaze was riveted on the steamboat.

Selena let her attention slide back to the boat, trying to disguise her sudden intense curiosity about the woman beside her. She couldn't stop herself from probing further.

"Have you ever taken a trip on the *Delta Queen?*" she asked, certain the woman didn't work for the company.

"Yes, I have...many times." There was the slightest pause in her words, the length of a heartbeat, leaving Selena with the impression that the woman had a catch in her voice.

With a sideways glance, she studied the woman again. Initially she saw the same image as before—an older woman, calm and composed and completely in control. Then Selena noticed the flaws.

A white linen handkerchief edged with lace was being twisted by agitated fingers. And the luminous quality of the woman's brown eyes was produced by a fine mist of tears. Too many times, members of her father's congregation had come to the parsonage, ostensibly for a friendly visit, only to have something in their behavior betray an inner turmoil, as this older woman was doing now.

15

Selena was not her father's daughter for nothing. "Excuse me, but—is something wrong?" Unconsciously she adopted the gentle, consoling tone she had so often heard her father use. She removed her sunglasses so the dark lenses would not shade the woman's reaction.

"I—" Instant denial formed on the woman's lips. As she caught sight of the compassion gleaming quietly in Selena's eyes, she checked the denouncement and turned away. "It's—nothing."

"I don't mean to be personal, but I can tell something is troubling you. Sometimes it helps to talk about it—to a stranger." Selena noticed the faint quivering in the woman's chin.

"You're a very astute young woman." The reply was accompanied by a stiff smile. "Not many people your age would be concerned enough to inquire," she sighed.

"It's probably a case of environment and upbringing." Selena dismissed the idea that she was in any way special, only different. "My father is a minister."

"That no doubt accounts for it." The woman glanced at her lace handker-chief and nervously tried to smooth out the wrinkles she had twisted into it.

"My name is Selena Merrick." Selena offered her hand to the woman.

"Julia Barkley," the woman returned, clasping Selena's hand warmly but briefly. "Are you here on vacation?"

"Yes. I'm your typical tourist, sight-seeing and all." Selena understood the woman's reluctance to confide in her and let the conversation take its own direction. "That's what brought me to the wharf. I heard the *Delta Queen* had docked and wanted to see her."

"Where is your home?"

"In Iowa," Selena acknowledged.

"Coming from the farmlands of the prairie, you probably don't mind the flatness of our delta land, do you?" the woman who had identified herself as Julia Barkley asked, smiling.

"No," Selena agreed with a wry twist of her curved lips, "although we do have more hills than you do. Do you live in New Orleans?"

"Actually my family's home is outside of New Orleans, but I keep a small apartment here so I can get away every once in a while to be on my own." Unconsciously the older woman stressed the words "get away."

Selena immediately guessed there were family problems at home, pos-sibly a daughter-in-law that Julia Barkley wasn't able to get along with. That thought became sidetracked as she caught the woman staring again at the massive paddle wheeler in an attitude that could only be described as wistfully reminiscent.

"You have a special attachment to the *Delta Queen*, don't you?" Selena observed softly. "Because of something that happened to you."

16

The woman's tears were in definite evidence, welling diamond bright in her eyes, but there was a radiant happiness, too, about her expression. Her reddened lips curved into a faint smile.

"I met Leslie on that boat," she whispered absently.

"Your husband?" Selena guessed.

"No." Julia Barkley blinked away her tears before glancing at Selena. "I'm not married. I'm the old maid of my family, literally," she tried to joke about her advanced years as Selena reacted with surprise. "That's why they think I'm being overly romantic and silly now. Women of my age aren't supposed to act the way I do."

"What do you mean?" Selena was thoroughly confused. Her guesses about the elderly woman and her family problems had obviously not been accurate.

"Do you believe in love at first sight, Selena?" she responded to the question with another question, then added, "may I call you Selena?"

"Of course you may, but as for your first question—" Selena laughed "— I'm not exactly an expert. I've never been in love before—a few near brushes here and there, but never the real thing. I have no idea if it can happen the first time you meet."

"Believe me, my dear, it can. It did for me—with Leslie." Her brown gaze swung again to the boat, distant and vaguely dreamy.

"What happened?" Selena dared the question.

"He asked me to marry him." A mixture of pain and confusion seemed to flicker across the woman's smooth forehead. It was quickly masked with a polite smile as Julia Barkley turned to Selena. "I was on my way to church. Would you like to join me? Afterward, if you have no other plans, perhaps you'll have Sunday dinner with me at my apartment? Don't hesitate to say no if you'd rather not come. I'll quite understand."

"I would like to come," Selena accepted without hesitation.

Despite the wealth and status implied by her clothes and manner, Julia Barkley was a lonely woman plagued at this moment by memories of a lost love. Selena sensed it as surely as if it had been put into words.

And Selena enjoyed people too much to even consider that a few hours in the older woman's company would prove boring. Besides, she had twelve full days of her vacation left, so what did a few hours on a Sunday matter?

Just for a moment, she imagined she could hear her mother laughing and exclaiming, "Stray dogs and orphans couldn't find a better home than with you, Selena." Even at twenty-three, Selena had to admit she was sometimes too trusting of strangers.

Look what had happened yesterday with the dark-haired man in the hotel passage. She smiled to herself. Obviously she hadn't learned a thing about strangers, because here she was going to dinner and church with

17

another. She pushed the thought of the tall, muscular man to the background of her mind.

It returned to haunt her at an inopportune moment. It had happened during the church service while the collection was being taken. Her handbag slipped from her lap, nearly spilling all its contents onto the floor before she could catch it. But the large denomination of bills the man had tucked in her purse did slide silently to the floor. Selena had forgotten all about the money until that embarrassing moment.

A frown of concern creased Julia Barkley's forehead as she whispered to Selena, "You shouldn't carry so much cash with you. It really isn't wise."

"It's n-not mine," Selena explained nervously and self-consciously. "I'm just keeping it for someone. I'll be returning it...later."

Just how, she wasn't sure, but she would think of some way to return the money to the man, short of knocking on his hotel room door, of course.

Fortunately Julia Barkley accepted her explanation. Or at least, she was too polite to question Selena about it any further.

At the conclusion of the church service, a car was waiting outside for them, a previous arrangement made by Julia Barkley before she had left her apartment.

But Selena was a bit confused when the car stopped at the canopied entrance of a building complete with a doorman. It had all the earmarks of a hotel. When she stepped out of the car, her suspicions were confirmed by the name, Hotel Ponchartrain.

"The hotel has suites they let on a permanent basis," Julia explained as they entered the marbled lobby.

It was a beautiful suite of rooms that Julia guided her to, a luxurious apartment filled with lovely, old furniture. Some of the pieces, Selena was positive, were valuable antiques. Yet it was a very comfortable place.

Selena was quick to attribute the atmosphere of the rooms to her hostess, who was both charming and friendly, if at times a bit preoccupied. Their dinner, an oven meal prepared in advance by Julia and served on genuine china, was simple and excellent.

As Selena helped clear the dishes from the table, she noticed a bedroom door ajar in the hallway. Selena happened to glance inside and her eyebrows lifted curiously at the suitcases and clothes covering the bed.

"Are you going on a trip, Julia?" she questioned, not wanting to stay if her hostess had more urgent plans to attend to.

Julia's hands trembled slightly as she set the china plates on the counter. "Do you know, I can't make up my mind?" The hiccupping sound that came from her throat was half laughter and half sob. "Isn't that silly?" She looked at Selena, tears gathering in her eyes again.

18

Not since they had left the wharf had Selena noticed any crack in the older woman's composure. Now it was there and widening.

"There are some decisions that are difficult to make at any age," Selena offered. She hesitated to probe, but she felt Julia wanted her to ask. "Were you planning to return home to your family?"

"No." Julia turned away to discreetly wipe the tears from her eyes and smooth the silvered wing of hair into the dark. "I have a passage booked on the *Delta Queen* tomorrow—to meet Leslie."

"Leslie?" Selena echoed, grateful the woman couldn't see her startled expression. For some reason she had thought Leslie was dead.

"Yes," she answered with a hesitant nod. "He's to meet me in Natchez— where we're to be married."

"Really?" This time Selena couldn't mask her incredulity. Then she saw the woman's tightly clutched fingers and the frown of pain wrinkling her brow. "You are going, aren't you?"

"I don't know," Julia murmured uncertainly, shaking her head.

"But you said you loved him." It was Selena's turn to frown.

"I do," the older woman hastened, then sighed in frustration. "I don't know what's the matter with me. I'm as nervous and unsure of myself as a schoolgirl."

In a gesture of bewilderment, Selena ran her fingers through the auburn hair near her ear. "I think there's some point in all of this that I'm missing. You love Leslie and he wants to marry you, but there seems to be something that's holding you back. What is it, Julia?"

"My family," the woman admitted. "My brother thinks I'm crazy. He insists that Leslie is only interested in the family money and the doors the Barkley name can open for him. My sister, everyone, agrees with him."

"Have they met him?"

"Oh, yes, they've met him," Julia assured her, and Selena realized it had been a foolish question to ask a woman of Julia's maturity and status. Of course, she would have introduced him to her family. "Leslie and I met on the *Delta Queen* during its autumn cruise last year. We corresponded for a time. In one of the letters, he proposed to me." Selena could well imagine that his letters were tied up in a pretty blue ribbon and secreted away in some safe place to be read over and over again. "I was so deliriously happy. I invited him to New Orleans after the winter holidays to meet my relatives. It was—" Julia stopped, unable to finish the sentence.

"Disastrous?" Selena completed it for her.

"Totally," Julia sighed the admission. "My brother, Hamilton, insisted there was too large a difference in our ages."

Selena gave an involuntary start of surprise. Was Leslie younger than Julia? It seemed unlikely at Julia's age—whether it was fifty-five or sixty—

19

that her brother should protest about her marrying a man fifteen or twenty years older.

If he was that age, what would Julia's status and money mean to Leslie? If a man in his seventies proposed to a woman in her sixties, Selena felt he should be applauded instead of condemned.

"And the rest of my family," Julia continued, "believes that I'm foolish to take this romantic fling, as they call it, seriously. They absolutely forbid me to have anything more to do with him."

"They forbid you?" Selena repeated. Surely the woman was old enough to behave or misbehave as she wanted. "You obviously didn't listen to them."

"No, though perhaps I should have," the woman murmured with a rueful twist of her mouth. "But I had to write him to explain why I couldn't marry him. Initially I did refuse him," she added in quick explanation. "Then Leslie wrote me back and I answered it. Before I knew it we were exchanging letters again. In one of his letters, he told me how much he loved me." There was a definite throb in Julia's voice as she added, "And how much he wanted me to be his wife, a-and suggested that we elope..."

"Now you can't decide whether you want to marry him or not," Selena concluded.

"Oh, I want to marry him. But my family—" Her voice trailed off, the tug-of-war still going on inside. She looked beseechingly at Selena. "What would you do?"

"Don't put me on a spot like that, Julia," she declared. It seemed impossible that a woman old enough to be her grandmother would be asking her, Selena, for advice about love and marriage.

"There isn't anyone else I can ask," the woman replied with a despairing shrug. "My family is so prejudiced against Leslie. You, at least, are impartial."

"You have to live your own life, Julia." Selena fell back on the advice her father had always given to her when she had sought him out. "Whatever decision you make will be the one you'll have to live with and not your family."

Julia murmured absently, "It's the things in life you don't do that you regret." She glanced at Selena and smiled. "That's what my nephew always says when my brother begins to lecture him about his questionable escapades."

"There's a great deal of truth in that," Selena agreed, thinking to herself that there was a member of the Barkley family who evidently didn't always obey the family's edict.

"Yes, and I would always regret it if I never saw Leslie again," Julia declared in a wistful sigh.

"I think you've just come up with your own solution," Selena smiled gently.

"I have?" she returned with a startled look.

"Take the trip and see Leslie again," Selena explained. "Maybe what you once felt for him won't be there anymore. You would still have time to back out before the marriage takes place."

"You're right. That's exactly what I will do!" The shadows left her brown eyes at last, leaving them clear and sparkling. "What would I have done without you, Selena?" Julia declared. "If I hadn't met you today—"

"You still would have made a decision," Selena interrupted, unwilling to take any credit for prompting Julia to a decision.

"But would it have been the right one? And I know in my heart that this one is right."

"I'm glad," Selena said, and meant it.

"I wish you were coming with me. I would so like to have you meet Leslie." The words were no sooner out of her mouth than Julia's expression brightened as an idea flashed through her mind. "Would you come, Selena?"

The request caught Selena completely by surprise. "I—" She couldn't seem to get any answer out.

"As crazy as it sounds, I've never traveled anywhere alone," Julia admitted with a self-deprecating laugh.

"Never?" echoed Selena, although she didn't know why she was astounded. Julia had obviously led an unusually sheltered life.

"Never. Sophie, my cousin, usually goes with me. She accompanied me on the cruise where I met Leslie."

"Well then, maybe she—" Selena began.

"Could come along this time?" Julia finished the phrase and laughed, a throaty, amused sound. "I think not. She despised Leslie. I think she was jealous. Sophie is a few years younger than I am and much more attractive, but Leslie didn't look at her once on the cruise."

It was unnecessary for Julia to explain that her cousin would violently oppose the elopement.

"I suppose it wouldn't be a good idea to have her go with you," Selena conceded.

"But I would enjoy it very much if you could come along, Selena. And I know you'd enjoy the cruise. It's eleven days up the Mississippi River into the Ohio to Cincinnati. There's entertainment and dancing aboard as well as other activities. And the *Delta Queen* stops at various river ports along the way, interesting and historical cities that I know you would like to see."

It did sound tempting, Selena admitted silently. She would certainly see more of the country than just New Orleans and more than the mile-high jet flight home would permit.

"I'm sure it would be very interesting," she admitted as she tried to find a gentle way to refuse the request. "But—"

21

"You did say you were on vacation," Julia reminded her, not appearing to understand Selena's hesitation.

"I am."

"How silly of me!" Julia exclaimed suddenly. "Of course, you're hesitant because of the cost. You mustn't worry about that, dear. I'll gladly pay your fare."

"It isn't a question of money. I can pay my own way," Selena asserted quickly.

"Gracious! Here I am making all these plans and I don't even know if there's a room available. Sometimes you have to make reservations for these cruises months in advance," Julia explained, as she walked toward the telephone in the small sitting room. "I'll call to see."

"But it's Sunday," was the only protest Selena could offer in her astonishment. She felt as if she was caught in a whirlwind.

Julia tossed her a twinkling glance that made her look very young. "This is one time when it's an advantage to have Barkley for a surname." And she picked up the telephone receiver.

Later that afternoon in her hotel room, Selena wondered how in the world Julia had succeeded in persuading her to go on the cruise. Somehow she had been gently bulldozed into agreeing. Not that she minded, since the cruise on the old steamboat sounded as if it would be interesting and unusual.

Selena had convinced Julia that she would pay her own way before she had left the apartment, assuring the older woman that she didn't require or expect financial assistance from her. Besides, the fare wasn't that much more than Selena had expected to pay for her hotel and meals during her stay in New Orleans.

She was to meet Julia at four o'clock the next afternoon at the riverboat terminal on the wharf. Glancing at her luggage, Selena was glad she had unpacked less than half of her clothes. It wouldn't take her long to pack, which meant she would have time to see more of New Orleans before she left. Flexibility had always been one of her key traits, she reminded herself.

However, there was one thing she had to take care of before she left. Opening her purse, she took out the folded bills and removed a hotel envelope from the drawer of the nightstand. The simplest and least risky way of returning the money to the man would be to slip it in an envelope under his door.

Sealing the money in the envelope, she reached for the telephone and dialed his room number. When it rang the fourth time with no answer, Selena was convinced the coast was clear and started to hang up.

The receiver was halfway to its cradle when an impatient male voice crackled into the room, "Yes?" Her hand froze guiltily. At her continued silence, the commanding male voice came over the phone again. "Who is this? What room were you calling?"

22

There was no question in her mind that the voice belonged to the man whose money she held in her hand. Very quietly, she hung up the telephone. She would have to wait until later to return it to him when there wasn't a chance of her being caught slipping the envelope under his door.

At midmorning on Monday, there was no answer when she dialed his room. With the envelope in hand, Selena left her room and started down the hallway to his. She nearly turned around and darted for the safety of her own room when she saw his door standing open. Then she heard the hum of a vacuum cleaner and walked closer. The maid was in the room cleaning.

Sighing in exasperation, Selena decided there had to be another way of getting the envelope to him. That was when it dawned on her that she could leave it at the desk for him. Immediately she took the elevator to the lobby.

"May I help you, miss?" One of the younger male clerks inquired when Selena approached the front desk. The sweeping look of admiration he gave her was thinly disguised behind a polite smile.

"Would it be possible to leave a message for one of your other guests?" Selena fingered the envelope nervously.

"Of course. What room number, please?" he requested with an intensely curious gleam in his eyes.

Selena gave it to him. He frowned and glanced at his records. "I'm sorry, miss, but that room is vacant."

"Vacant? But there was a gentleman—" she began.

"He checked out this morning," the clerk explained.

Selena nibbled at the inside of her lower lip for a thoughtful second, then asked, "Would you give me his name and address, please, so I could mail it to him?"

"I'm sorry, miss," he said smiling apologetically, "but the hotel isn't permitted to give out that information."

"I see," she murmured dejectedly, and managed a smile. "Thank you."

As she walked slowly away from the desk, she wondered what she was going to do with the money. She couldn't keep it, that was certain. But now it was impossible to return it to him. That only left one choice—to give it away to a charitable institution where it would do some good.

She walked to the nearest phone booth and copied the name and address of a local branch of a national organization onto the envelope. With a postage stamp from her purse, she stuck it in the corner and dropped the envelope in the hotel's mailbox.

A wry smile tugged at the edges of her mouth. At least the incident had ended on a redeeming note, she thought.

3

ollowing Julia Barkley over the gangplank onto the boat, Selena felt a rush of excitement and nostalgia fill her. If it wasn't for the orange Volkswagen with the black letters Steamer Delta Queen painted on its doors that was parked on the bow of the boat, she could have been stepping into another era.

Polished wood gleamed darkly in the wide stairwell leading to the second deck of the boat where fellow passengers were milling around the large and gracious sitting room. Julia didn't pause to let Selena take in the furnishings but continued straight to the purser's office at the end of the room.

A tall, uniformed man was talking to one of the porters, but when his ever-roving gaze touched on Julia Barkley, a smile wreathed his face. With a quick word to the white-coated porter, he stepped forward to meet her, extending his hand.

"Miss Julia, it's good to have you aboard with us again," he declared with beaming sincerity. "I understand congratulations are in order," he winked, and squeezed Julia's hand.

Selena smiled at the blush that colored the older woman's cheeks. It made her look very youthful and vulnerable and also very happy. "Yes, they are,

Douglas. Thank you," Julia said. "And it's good to be aboard the *Delta Queen* again. How is your father?"

"He's fine, Miss Julia, just fine." His blue eyes flicked their attention to Selena, then beyond her. "Where's your cousin, Miss Sophie? Isn't she with you?"

"No, not this time. She wasn't able to come. But Selena—Miss Merrick— is traveling with me." Julia turned to draw Selena forward. "Selena, this is the chief purser, Douglas Spender."

"We're pleased to have you aboard with us, Miss Merrick," he said as he shook her hand.

Selena had the distinct impression that he meant it and was not simply issuing polite words of welcome. Neither, on the other hand, was he making a pass. In his midforties, he was a tall and slender man with brown hair and blue eyes. There was a pleasant drawl to his voice and a decidedly charming way to his manner. Selena decided that she liked him.

"I know I'm going to enjoy it." Her smile widened into dimples.

"This is your first cruise?" he inquired.

"Yes," Selena nodded.

"Then I and my crew will do everything we can to insure that it will be enjoyable for you," he smiled. He clasped his hands in front of him in a gesture of decision. "I'm sure you'll want to see your cabins. Kevin—" he motioned to one of the porters, a young fair-haired man "—would you show Miss Julia and Miss Merrick to their cabins?"

"Yes, sir." He smiled at both of them, his gaze lingering a fraction of a second longer on Selena's youthful face. "This way, please, ladies." He led them through an opened door into the wide, interior passageway leading to cabins on the same deck. "You have your customary stateroom, Miss Julia," he said, pausing in front of a door numbered 109 to open it with a key before handing it to the older woman, "Your luggage is already inside. Is there anything else you'd like right now?"

"No, I don't believe so, Kevin." Julia smiled and glanced at Selena. "I'll meet you in the forward cabin in about twenty minutes."

"Fine," Selena agreed, then frowned in bewilderment after Julia had closed the door.

"Are you wondering where the forward cabin is?" the porter asked grinning.

"Yes," she laughed with a trace of self-consciousness.

"You just left it," he explained. "It's the sitting room where you met Doug Spender, the chief purser."

"Thank you." She glanced over her shoulder, hoping to keep her bearings.

"Your cabin is 237, up on the texas deck, Miss Merrick. I'll take you there now." The porter reclaimed her attention.

She followed him as he led her down the passageway, smiling to herself.

"Where is the texas deck?" she asked.

"One floor up."

"I'm never going to get these terms straight," Selena demurred.

"It's easy. You're on the cabin deck," he explained. "Front and back are forward and aft or bow and stern. After a few days on board, they'll come naturally to you."

"I hope so," Selena murmured with a skeptical smile. He was dealing with a landlocked girl from Iowa!

He turned right down the short hall toward an exit door leading to the outer passageway. There was also a door on the opposite side of the boat, Selena noticed.

As he turned to make certain she was behind him, the porter saw her glance at the other door. "We'll use this one," he said, pushing the door open. "Watch your step." He indicated the raised threshold over which Selena carefully stepped. "The odd-numbered cabins are on the port side of the boat," he said, explaining his reason for using this exit.

"Oh, dear!" Selena laughed softly.

Walking only a half a step ahead of her, he turned his blond head to give her an understanding grin. "As you face the bow of the boat—the front—the port side is left and the starboard is right."

"Of course," she nodded, but the sparkling gleam in her eyes said she would never remember and the porter laughed, his gaze openly admiring. As they ascended the covered stairwell to the next deck, Selena said, "I know I'm being foolish because I'll probably forget your answer, but why is it called the texas deck?"

"It's texas deck with a small 't'. It's customary on a riverboat for the largest deck to be called the texas deck after the largest state, Texas. At least at the time of the riverboats, it was the largest state," he explained. "And staterooms derived their names from the fact that they, were named after states—the Kentucky Room, the Vermont Room, and so on."

"Fascinating," murmured Selena.

At the top of the stairs he stopped, producing a key from his pocket. "Your room, Miss Metrick," he announced and opened the door.

"Thank you." She nodded, and added with a smile, "And thank you for the lessons, too."

"Definitely my pleasure," he declared, and handed her the key.

With a bobbing nod to her, he turned to retrace his steps. Selena hesitated, then stepped over the raised threshold into her cabin.

A single chest of drawers stood against the wall just inside the door. Two single berths flanked the room. Her luggage was sitting on the floor at the foot of the bed, her garment bag hanging on a clothes rod in the corner. A full-length mirror covered the door leading to the bathroom. The room was compact and efficient and very comfortably adequate.

Unpacking only the clothes that had a tendency to wrinkle, Selena left the rest of it till later. She freshened her lipstick and ran a brush over her copper hair. Slipping her room key into her bag, she left the cabin a few minutes ahead of the agreed time to find her way to the forward cabin lounge. She retraced the exact route the porter had taken and met Julia just as she was stepping out of her stateroom.

"Selena, come see what was waiting for me in my room," Julia exclaimed with delight.

Following Julia into her cabin, Selena stopped just inside the room. A dozen long-stemmed roses glowed velvet red from their crystal vase atop the dresser.

"They're beautiful, Julia," Selena smiled, knowing instinctively that the bouquet was what the older woman had wanted her to see.

"They're from Leslie, of course." There was extra warmth in her voice as she said his name. "Here's the card that came with them."

She handed Selena a small envelope, opened to reveal the card inside. Selena read the personal message written on it somewhat self-consciously. The words were simple but eloquently touching. "I love you, Julia. May I always and forever be—your Leslie." Silently she handed it back to Julia. All the comments that came to her mind seemed inadequate and trite.

Julia read it again before slipping it back in its envelope. "It's moments like this that make me wonder why I have any doubts," she sighed. Again Selena couldn't think of a suitable response and remained silent. As if pulling herself out of her reverie, Julia turned to Selena, fixing a bright smile on her face. "Have you done a bit of exploring yet?"

"No, not yet," Selena admitted. "With all the coming and going of passengers and crew, it's a bit crowded and confusing."

"That's true. And there'll be plenty of time for you to discover every nook and corner of the boat before the cruise is over," Julia stated with a knowing gleam in her brown eyes. "Since the weather is so nice, shall we go up to the texas lounge? Perhaps there'll be a table free. We can relax and have a glass of sherry."

"Sounds fine," Selena agreed.

In the interior passageway, Julia stopped to obtain their table assignment in the dining room from the head waiter before continuing, with Selena at her side, to the forward cabin lounge. Stopping abruptly just inside the lounge, Selena breathed in sharply at the sight of the grand staircase leading to the texas lounge.

"It takes your breath away, doesn't it?" Julia commented.

"Indeed it does," Selena declared, staring at the gleaming wood columns that stood regally at the fanning base of the stairs.

Brass kickboards shimmered gold on the steps. The sweeping curve of the banister railings was inset with lacy scrolled wrought iron. An arched opening had been carved into the ceiling and a chandelier suspended in the aperture.

"I expect to see Rhett Butler appear any minute and carry me up the stairs," Selena confided to Julia in a somewhat awestruck tone.

"Yes, it does remind one of the 'grand old manor' and the days of gracious living," Julia agreed, moving forward to ascend the stairs. "In her day, the *Delta Queen* was the epitome of luxury living and modern conveniences. Her woodwork and paneling is all oak or mahogany. Of course, most of it's covered now with fire retardant paint—Coast Guard regulations."

"It's a pity." Selena observed all the wood moldings and paneling that were painted a cream white.

"It's a compromise with modern times and the need for passenger safety, but it doesn't diminish her charm."

"It certainly doesn't." Selena could already feel the gentle atmosphere warmly enveloping her.

The sensation was intensified as she reached the top of the grand staircase and entered the horseshoe-shaped texas lounge, windowed all around. The rich luster of the wood was free of paint, its casual elegance enhanced by the plaid carpet underfoot.

Furnished with small square tables and captain's chairs, the room had a bar with tall stools in the center of its horseshoe. Double doors on either side of the room opened onto the outer deck where white wrought-iron tables and chairs were waiting.

As Selena and Julia walked toward one set of double doors, a bartender leaned over the bar. "Hi, Miss Julie. I heard you were aboard."

After an initial blank look, surprised recognition flashed across the woman's strong features. "Greg! I didn't expect you to be here. I thought you were quitting to go to college."

"I was." He ducked under the narrow opening cut into the side of the bar and walked over to meet them. "But I decided it would be financially wiser to work through the summer and sign up for the fall term."

"Be sure that you do," Julia insisted in a matronly tone. "You need to complete your education."

Light brown eyes swung to Selena to regard her with studied intentness. Despite his full brown mustache, Selena decided he wasn't any older than she was, possibly a year or two younger. He was good-looking, and there was something in his expression that said he knew it. His charm was evident in his engaging smile and his slow, drawling way of talking.

"Is this your niece, Miss Julie?" he asked, his gaze remaining fixed on Selena.

"No, Miss Merrick is a friend. This is Greg Simpson, an incorrigible but likable young man," Julia introduced them. "And the only one who uses the diminutive of my name, irrespective of my wishes."

"Miss Julie, you know you like it," he chided teasingly, and Selena guessed he was right, judging by the twinkle in Julia's otherwise sternly composed face.

"If I didn't know how hard you work in this job, I would say you rely too heavily on sweet talking," Julia stated.

The bartender laughed off her words of reproof and smiled at Selena. "How do you do, Miss Merrick. And welcome aboard the *Delta Queen.*"

"Thank you," she nodded.

"The chief purser, Doug Spender, gave orders that your first sherry of the cruise was to be on him, Miss Julie," he announced, swinging his attention back to the older woman. "Would you like it on the outer deck?"

"Please," Julia agreed.

He turned to Selena. "And what would you like to drink, courtesy of the chief purser?"

Hesitating for a fraction of a second, she said, "I'll have the same."

"My name is Greg," he offered in invitation of its use. "We'll be living together aboard this boat for the next ten days, so we might as well start right out with first names."

"Very well, Greg," Selena agreed, her naturally outgoing nature accepting his friendly advance.

"I'm sorry, but I'm afraid I've forgotten your first name," Greg smiled.

"That's because I didn't give it to you," Julia inserted dryly.

Selena supplied it with a laugh, "It's Selena."

"I like it," he winked before moving off toward the bar. "Two sherries coming right up."

"Incorrigible!" Julia clicked reprovingly under her breath, but Selena noticed the indulgent gleam in the older woman's eye.

On the outer deck, the air was humid and still with only an occasional breath of breeze to stir it. Seated in the wrought-iron deck chair, Selena enjoyed the warmth of the late-afternoon sun on her face.

Her back was to the doors of the texas lounge as she faced the Mississippi River. She missed Greg's approach until he was at their table setting their sherry glasses on cocktail napkins.

His gaze touched the fiery crown of Selena's hair, flaming brighter in the sunlight. "If there's anything else, just call me," he said as he withdrew.

More passengers were migrating toward the lounge, some of them spilling onto the deck where Selena and Julia sat. Their happy, laughing voices were in keeping with the bustling activity Selena was witnessing on the river.

29

A large oil tanker was moving slowly up the river while other ships, freighters mostly, were docked along the wharves. There seemed to be an almost constant stream of towboats pushing barges up or down the river. In the middle of all this activity, the ferryboat to Algiers was darting back and forth across the Mississippi.

Selena was absorbed by the river scene until she heard a sharply indrawn gasp from Julia. She glanced at the older woman curiously and frowned at the dismay in the woman's expression. Her concern was immediate.

"Julia, what's wrong?"

"It's my nephew. He's here." She bit at her lower lip, her gaze focused on an object beyond Selena. "I should have known my brother would send him to try to stop me!"

Selena didn't want to be caught in the middle of a family dispute. "I'll leave so you can speak to him alone." She started to rise, but Julia lifted a hand to stop her.

"Please stay," she requested with a hint of panic in her low voice. "I'm afraid I'll need your moral support."

There didn't seem to be any way to refuse without appearing heartless. After the way Julia had befriended her, Selena knew she couldn't treat the older woman that way. But she promised herself she wouldn't become any further involved as she sat back in her chair, aware of the firm, steady strides approaching the table.

"Hello, Julia." At the sound of the male voice, cold fingers ran down Selena's spine.

It couldn't possibly be the same man who had propositioned her in the hallway of the hotel, her mind cried in disbelief. Her fingers closed around the stem of her sherry glass, shock waves vibrating through her body.

"What a surprise to see you here, Chance." Julia's voice wavered as she greeted the man.

Selena dared an upward glance at the man who had stopped at their table. Her look was returned, coal black eyes hard with recognition, slicing her to the bone before directing their attention to the older woman seated opposite Selena. With an alacrity that surprised her, he assumed an expression of gentleness and patience.

"Is it a surprise, Julia?" There was affection in his mocking tone.

"How did you know where to find me?" the older woman sighed heavily.

Part of Selena wanted to bolt for safety, but she remained rooted to the chair. Staring blindly at her glass, she was uncomfortably aware of the thoughts and opinions that were probably going through the man's mind. She tried to comfort herself with the knowledge that she had been the innocent victim of an unfortunate set of circumstances, but it didn't lessen the disturbance trembling through her.

"I stopped by your apartment," he answered his aunt's question. "The girl at the desk told me you'd left on a trip. After that, it was simple deduction that brought me here."

"I suppose Hamilton sent you," Julia declared with a trace of resentment.

"Yes, he was hoping I would be able to persuade you not to do this," he admitted.

"He should mind his own business." Agitation quivered in Julia's reply, drawing Selena's gaze to the moisture glistening in the liquid-brown eyes.

"Hamilton is your brother. It's natural for him to be concerned about you and what you're doing with your life," was the calmly reasoning response. Selena sensed that he was choosing his words with care, not wanting too much of the family linen to be aired in front of her.

"But it is my life. And I want to do this, it's my right," Julia insisted with a traitorous lack of conviction in the strong words.

"He doesn't want you to be hurt—none of us does. What you're doing is foolish and it's only going to bring unnecessary anguish. Come home with me now, before it goes any further." His tone was cajolingly persuasive. Even Selena could feel its pull. "I—"

"Chance," Julia interrupted to protest, "you know how I feel about Leslie."

"Julia—" Impatience flashed in his voice, making Selena's gaze lift to see the grimness in his features.

"No," Julia stopped the rest of his sentence. "I know what you're going to say. I've heard it all before and it isn't going to change the way I feel. Please, I'm going to do this," she appealed to him to understand. "Don't try to talk me out of it."

Covertly, Selena watched his reaction to the plea. At first there was a stubborn set to the sharply etched line of his jaw, his narrowed black gaze unrelenting.

Then suddenly his eyes smiled. There was no other way to describe the change in his expression. There was no movement of his mouth, nothing except his eyes crinkling at the corners.

"All right, I've tried. My duty to the family is done," he stated. "All that's left is to have a bon-voyage drink with you and the young lady."

There was no smile in his eyes as his gaze swung to Selena. Only a faint challenge glittered through the black shutter he had pulled over them. It was his first formal acknowledgement of her existence and Selena felt trapped. Every nerve end tautened into alertness.

"Where are my manners?" Julia exclaimed in embarrassed agitation, and she hastened to correct her omission of an introduction, one that Selena would rather have avoided. "Selena, this is my nephew, Chance Barkley. Chance, this is a new friend, Selena Merrick."

"How do you do, Mr. Barkley." The words sounded stilted and cold even to her own ears.

"Miss Merrick." He made a mocking half bow to acknowledge her greeting, his gaze hard and glittering as it rested on her upturned face. Drawing an empty chair to the table, he directed his next remark to his aunt. "She must be a very new friend of yours, since I don't recall ever seeing her with you."

There was the faintest emphasis on the last two words, but Selena heard it, as Chance Barkley had guessed she would.

"Oh, yes, as a matter of fact we just met this weekend," Julia admitted.

The upward flick of his dark brow seemed to say, "You, too." Selena felt like squirming in her seat. It didn't help that he was aware of her discomfiture and was enjoying it.

"You must have a facility for making new friends easily." If it was possible for a man's voice to purr like a smug cat, his did.

His double-edged meaning was not lost on her. "I try, Mr. Barkley," she retorted in a voice riddled with fine tension.

"Call me Chance. You see—" again the taunting smile returned to laugh at her predicament "—already I feel as if I've met you before."

Troubled, green-flecked eyes lowered their attention to the quirking line of his mouth, which was subtly drawn, very masculine and provoked the memory of his potent, drugging kisses. Unnerved, Selena curled her fingers around the glass, ordering her hand not to tremble as she lifted it to her lips. A gulp of the amber-brown wine didn't dull her senses, which leaped in alarm.

His glittering regard was distracted by the appearance of the bartender, Greg, at the table. "Would you like something to drink, sir?"

"Scotch. Chivas Regal on the rocks." Chance Barkley leaned back in his chair, relaxed and insolent, but Selena knew it was only a pose. Despite those lazily drooping eyelids, he was just as alert as she was.

"Very good, sir," Greg nodded. "And how about you, Miss Julie? Would you care for another sherry?"

"One is my limit, Greg," she replied in an apparent reminder.

"Yes, ma'am," he smiled and turned to Selena, his light brown eyes flirting with her—a fact Chance Barkley was quick to note, sardonic mockery flicking across his chiseled male features. "And you, Selena?"

She stared at the glass her fingers circled and the sherry that barely covered the bottom. "Nothing, Greg, thanks," she answered stiffly.

When Greg left, Chance said, "I'm curious. How did the two of you meet?"

"Here," Julia answered. At his sharply questioning look, she laughed and explained, "We met on the dock. We'd both come to see the *Delta Queen* when she docked. We started talking, then one thing led to another, and I invited Selena to church and Sunday dinner."

"To church?"

If he had laughed aloud, his ridiculing amusement couldn't have been more evident as his derisive gaze swung to Selena. Her chin lifted in defensive challenge.

Julia seemed ignorant of the byplay. "Yes, Selena is a minister's daughter."

"Really? I would never have guessed." His voice was bland, but the jeering light in his eyes raked her with contempt. Selena burned slowly in helpless anger, unable to find convincing words to offer in her own defense.

"We had a very enjoyable time together yesterday," Julia went on blithely. "And when I decided I was going to take this trip, I—"

"It was only yesterday that you decided to go on this trip?" Chance questioned sharply, looking at his aunt with thoughtful contemplation.

"I d-did have a few doubts before then," Julia hesitated, glancing anxiously at Selena. "But it was entirely my own decision."

Selena winced inwardly. Julia wasn't a very good liar, even though her statement was half true. Selena knew she had influenced the decision, however inadvertently, and Julia's assertion to the contrary held a false note. Selena saw the slight flaring of his nostrils as Chance Barkley heard it, otherwise he masked his reaction completely.

"In fact," Julia went on, as if to cover her previous words, "once I decided to go, I convinced Selena that she should come, too." At the harmless and completely true statement, Chance Barkley's gaze narrowed into black diamond chips, slicing over Selena. "You know how I hate to travel alone, Chance." She smiled at Selena. "And Selena is such good company."

"How fortunate that your work permits you to take off at a moment's notice." His smiling comment was double-edged, its sharp side gibing at Selena to remind her of his knowledge of her alleged profession.

"I came here on vacation," she retorted.

"Everyone needs one now and again," Chance stated with an expressive shrug, the hard glint not leaving his eyes, "regardless of his or her line of work."

It was on the tip of Selena's tongue to inform him of her true occupation, but Greg's arrival with Chance's drink checked the words. When he left, Selena decided it would be useless to tell him. Chance Barkley would simply assume that it was a story she had concocted to make herself appear respectable in Julia's eyes, and would make her the recipient of more of his mocking scorn.

"Aren't you concerned that you might find this cruise boring, Selena?" Chance sipped at his drink, making his query with apparent nonchalance.

"I think it will be interesting," Selena countered. "Why should it be boring?"

"Haven't you noticed?" He swirled the ice cubes in his glass, glancing at her over its top and making her aware of his powerfully handsome features. "The majority of your fellow passengers belong to my aunt's generation."

33

"That won't be a deterrent to my enjoyment of the cruise, Mr. Barkley—"

"Chance," he corrected.

"Chance." Her teeth grated as she uttered his name, pinning a cool smile on her mouth.

There was something coldly calculating in the look he returned that made her want to panic. She sensed a determination in the makeup of his character that could border on ruthlessness if the situation warranted it.

But she couldn't gauge just how vengeful he felt over that incident in his hotel room and the money she hadn't been able to return to him. If only she hadn't been so quick to mail that money to a charity, she could have handed it over to him and vindicated herself to some degree.

The hoarse whistle of the steamboat blew a long and two shorts, hesitated and repeated the sequence. At its cessation a monotone voice issued an announcement over the public-address system.

"All ashore that's going ashore. All aboard that's coming aboard."

"Oh, dear," Julia murmured ruefully. "That means you have to leave, Chance."

"So it does," he agreed with a certain grimness. He downed most of his drink, setting the glass on the table as he pushed himself to his feet. He towered beside Julia's chair. "There isn't anything I can say to persuade you to come home with me?"

"No." She shook her head in negative answer to his half statement, half question. "Don't be angry with me, Chance," she pleaded softly.

A warm and gentle smile softened the hard contours of his face, crinkling his eyes. "I'm not angry, Julia, never with you. You should know that."

"Perhaps," she conceded, with a wealth of affection gleaming in her brown eyes as she gazed up at him. "But it makes me feel better to hear you say it."

Bending down, he kissed her rouged cheek. Selena glimpsed the springing thickness of black hair curling around his white collar. As Chance straightened, his gaze sought Selena. Briefly he inclined his head in her direction and walked away, disappearing into the interior of the texas lounge.

What had it been—a concession? Selena wondered. She was fully aware that she had been spared because she was with Julia. The boat would be leaving in a few minutes or he might have separated her from Julia. And that might have been very humiliating and difficult.

"Chance is almost like a son to me," Julia remarked, pride and sadness mixing in her expression. "He used to call me his 'other mother'. He was always so protective when he was young. He still is, in his own way. It wasn't fair of Hamilton to send Chance to stop me."

"He did seem very fond of you." Selena knew her remark was inadequate, but none other came to mind.

"Yes, he's often said that his mother and I are the only women he needs in his life on a permanent basis." Julia sipped at her sherry, thoughtful and vaguely reminiscent. "Not that he has much time for a private life now that Hamilton has turned everything over to him except the stud farm. And Chance hasn't been content to just manage. He's had to build and expand, take risks and experiment. Never foolishly, you understand."

Selena nodded. She suddenly felt weak and nerveless. She finished the last of her sherry, hoping it would somehow fortify her. It didn't. She hadn't realized how much of a strain she had been under until this minute. It had been like waiting for a bomb to go off and discovering it was a dud. It left her shaky and limp inside.

Assured by the nod that Selena was listening, Julia continued her dissertation. "Chance always holds on with one hand and reaches out to take what he wants with the other. Of course, he's always willing to pay the price. He doesn't expect to get it for free." Selena paled at that—the words were coming too close to her own experience. "I've often wondered if his name had anything to do with the type of man he is. I suppose not, because his grandfather was very much like Chance, too—willing to take risks."

"I hope he's a good loser," Selena commented.

"Oh, he is," Julia insisted. "Before he makes a move, he weighs the odds. No matter how much he loses, Chance doesn't blink an eye because he's already considered that possibility from the first. Unless he's been cheated, then it's an entirely different matter."

And he believed she had cheated him. Her stomach fluttered queasily. A series of wheezing discordant notes sounded from the stern of the riverboat, distracting Julia from her subject.

"Listen! They're going to start the calliope concert. Would you like to walk to the sun deck? There's also a welcome-aboard party in the aft cabin lounge if you'd rather attend it," Julia suggested as if suddenly aware her younger companion might prefer something more in the way of entertainment than listening to an old woman's ramblings.

"Actually, Julia, I think I would prefer to go to my room. I'd like to shower and do some unpacking before dinner," Selena said with an unsteady smile.

"You go right ahead, my dear. Dinner is at seven in the Orleans Room. We're seated at table 40."

The band had finished playing in the texas lounge, although the banjo player was plunking out a few notes as Selena made her way around the bow of the boat to the side of the texas deck where her cabin was located. For a time, the banjo vied with the calliope notes—festive sounds. Soon the texas lounge was behind Selena, and all she heard was the calliope.

Pausing at the railing outside her cabin, she didn't feel very festive. In the windows of the river terminal building where they were docked, she could see the reflection of the passengers gathered on the top deck listening to the musical steam whistles of the calliope. Her gaze strayed to the spectators scattered along the dock below her.

A little girl waved to her and Selena smiled and waved back, the smile soon fading to a faint curve. Her gaze wandered the length of the dock forward to the gangplank. There it was arrested by the tall, muscular figure of Chance Barkley, standing with his hand thrust negligently in his pants pocket, talking with the security guard on duty at the gangway.

As if he possessed an inner radar attuned to her, Chance turned his head, seeming to look directly at her. Shaken, Selena stared back, a fiery heat licking through her veins.

A gambler of sorts, Julia had called him. Selena conceded that he had some of the necessary qualities: the facile charm to trip the innocent; the unrelenting confidence to bluff his opponent; and the black shutters that could keep any of his thoughts from being revealed in his eyes.

Perhaps most of all Chance Barkley had a certain aura of danger about him gained from taking risks, a calculating recklessness that attracted. Combine that with his vital maleness and hard good looks and the end result was potent.

The dark head turned back to the guard, releasing Selena from his ensnarling gaze. She pivoted abruptly, searching through her purse for the cabin key. Her hand shook as she inserted it in the lock and opened the door.

4

The shower had the necessary reviving effect on Selena, leaving her flesh alive and tingling. Slipping into clean undergarments and her lemon yellow housecoat, she stepped into the main area of the cabin. With the louvered wood insets raised, she couldn't see out of the window.

Walking over, she slid the shutter halfway down. Instead of looking out through the glass at the windowed terminal building, she saw a strip of brown river water and a large freighter docked in from of one of the warehouses that lined the river.

How strange, she thought. There was no sensation of movement at all. Then she listened and heard the rhythmic thump of the engines, distantly, almost a vibration instead of a sound.

She turned from the window after raising the louver and walked to the chest of drawers. The hands of her traveling alarm clock said twenty minutes to seven, ample time to dress before dinner. Picking up her hairbrush, she began stroking the bristles through her hair until it was crackling and glistening like burnished copper.

A sharp rap at her cabin door brought a puzzled frown to her forehead. She hesitated, still holding the hairbrush in her hand.

"Who is it?" she called, certain Julia wouldn't be there.

"The steward," came the response, partially muffled by the door between them.

The wing of a brow lifted in confusion. Setting her brush on the dresser, Selena glanced over her shoulder to see if any of her luggage was missing. It was all there. With a little shrug of bewilderment, she reached for the door, unlocking the deadbolt and holding onto the knob to open the door a crack.

With the first sliver of outside light running the length of the door, it was yanked from her hand. In the next second, she was pushed backward. Her startled cry ended the instant she recognized the towering bulk. The door was shut.

"You!" she choked, her hazel eyes blazing with green flecks as they met the glittering black lights shining from Chance Barkley's eyes.

"I think we have some unfinished business, you and I." His voice was threateningly low.

Her hands were doubled into fists. She was too surprised and angry at the way he constantly kept popping up to be afraid. She stamped her bare foot in rage.

"Get out of here! Get out of my cabin this minute!" she ordered in a hissing rush.

"I don't think I will," he said, defying her complacently and taking a step toward her.

Instinctively she backed up. An ashtray sat on the small, narrow shelf beside the bed. She grabbed for it, desperate fingers clutching the smooth glass.

"Keep away from me!" She hurled it at his head.

He ducked and the ashtray careened loudly off the door frame, bouncing intact onto the carpeted floor. Her blood was thundering like an express train through her veins, her breath coming in quick, short gasps. She reached for the ashtray on the shelf on the opposite wall.

Long, talon-strong fingers caught her wrist, jerking her away and capturing her other wrist. Her straining and twisting struggles were wasted as Chance hauled her effortlessly against his chest.

"Didn't your mother ever teach you not to throw things, Red?" The low, taunting voice was smooth and complacent. "You could have hurt me with that ashtray."

"I wish it had bashed your head in!" Selena declared, and gasped in pained surprise as he twisted her arms behind her back and crushed her soft shape to his length.

"You're a bloodthirsty little thief," he reproved mockingly.

"Let me go or I'll scream," she threatened, tilting her head back to glare at him. "I mean it!"

He shifted the position of her arms behind her back, the long fingers of one hand easily gripping both wrists. "We can't have that," he murmured.

And Selena realized he was ignoring her warning. Taking a quick breath, she opened her mouth to scream, but his free hand was at the back of her head, holding it still while he smothered her cry in a punishing kiss. Valiantly Selena resisted, muted cries and words of damnation coming from her throat, to be swallowed by his mouth.

Powerless against his superior strength, she kicked at his shins with her bare feet, nearly breaking her toe. He forced her backward, somehow lifting her feet off the floor. She writhed against him and realized with sickening panic that the buttons that had always been too small for the buttonholes of her robe were beginning to slip free from the material in her struggle.

That discovery was quickly replaced by another, one as alarming as the first. With a balancing knee on the mattress, Chance was lowering her to the bed. Waves of panic swamped her, almost paralyzing her lungs and her heart. She glimpsed a ray of hope. As the solidness of the bed formed beneath her, he released her wrists.

Selena didn't question his reason, but took advantage of it to bring her arms around, spreading her hands against his chest before his weight crushed her. He seemed content to let her stop him stretching his length beside her, even slackening his hold on her neck to permit her to twist away from his bruising mouth.

With her lips throbbing from the grinding kiss, Selena tried to roll away from the tautly muscled man lying beside her, but his large hand covered her hipbone to force her back. She realized with a start that that wasn't all his hand was doing. It was dispensing with the last remaining buttons of her robe.

"No, don't!" she gasped in panic.

"Such modesty, Red?" His throaty voice laughed at her attempt to stave off his hands as they pushed aside the covering robe. "You act as though I haven't seen you before similarly unclad."

Her mind whirled desperately, wildly seeking an answer, thoughts jumbling one on top of the other, making no sense. The only coherent thought that pierced her confusion was that Chance wasn't even supposed to be here.

"Why aren't you in New Orleans where you belong?" Selena accused breathlessly, "Don't you know the boat has left port?"

"Yes, I know." He was nibbling at her collarbone.

Her face was turned against the pillow as she struggled to stop his roving hands. Her nerve ends were tingling where his firm mouth explored, his warm breath caressing her sensitive skin.

"You were off the boat. I saw you," she declared on a frantic note. His attention had shifted to the pulsing vein in her neck with disturbing effect. "How did you get back on?"

"I slipped aboard when no one was looking," Chance murmured against her skin.

"What?" Selena was certain she hadn't understood him, the clamoring of her other senses possibly dulling her hearing.

She stopped trying to ward off his wayward hands. The priority had shifted to ending the devastation those male lips were wreaking. Her hands cupped his smoothly shaven jaws to push his face away as she twisted her head to bury her chin in her neck.

Selena partially succeeded in lifting his head, her fingers slipping into the midnight black of his hair. The silky crispness of the thick, strands curled around her fingers and against her palms, the feel of it virtually sensual.

"I stowed away," drawled Chance, and began an intimate exploration of her face, the wing of her brow and the curving sweep of her lashes. "You'll have to hide me."

Her fluttering lashes sprang open at the last low statement, while her hands slipped to his shoulder, splayed and resisting. "I'll do no such thing!" she denied hotly. "I'll turn you over to the captain and he'll put you ashore immediately."

Lifting his head a few inches, he studied her lazily, mockery glinting in his jet dark eyes at indignant flames flashing in hers. His hand raised to cup the underside of her jaw, his thumb rubbing the point of her chin.

There was something threatening in his action, as if at any provocation, his thumb would slide down to throttle her throat. Like a wild animal, Selena sensed the danger, saw it in the straight, ruthless line of his mouth, and remained warily motionless under his stroking thumb.

"If you turned me over to the captain, Red, I'd simply have to tell him about you." His thumb slid upward to move across her trembling lips as he added, "and the money you stole from me."

Swallowing, Selena tightly insisted, "I didn't steal your money." Her lips moved against his thumb as she spoke. It was not an altogether unpleasant sensation.

His veiled look focused on her mouth, sending her pulse rocketing, while his thumb directed itself to a more thorough exploration of her lower lip. His expression was completely masked as his gaze flicked to the round alertness of her eyes.

"Am I supposed to regard the red dress and shoes you left as equal to the value of the money you took?" he inquired in soft challenge. "Neither of them happen to be in my size or my color."

"That isn't what I meant," Selena protested.

40

"Then what did you mean?" His voice was as smooth as polished steel. "I gave you the money—you took it. And I didn't get what I paid for. I don't like being conned, Red. Nobody cheats me and gets away with it."

Selena could feel the silent menace of his words. "I didn't mean to take your money." With an effort, she kept her voice calm and firm.

"Didn't you?" A black eyebrow arched in mocking skepticism as his thumb moved away from her mouth.

"Honestly, I didn't," she insisted with a trace of taut anger. "When I grabbed my purse, I'd forgotten you'd put the money in it. All I was interested in was my room key that was in it."

"Your room key? You had a room at the hotel?"

"Yes, I was staying there."

"How convenient for your clients," Chance drawled.

"I don't have any clients," Selena retorted in exasperation. "It was all a joke."

"Then why am I not laughing?" he countered.

"Because you took everything seriously," she explained earnestly, her brows drawing together in a slight frown.

"When money is involved, I'm always serious." Flat black eyes regarded her steadily and her own faltered under the look.

"Look, it was all a mistake," she began nervously. "I'm—"

But Chance interrupted to derisively mock, "A minister's daughter?"

"From Iowa," Selena tacked on unconsciously.

Laughter rolled from his throat, rich and deep, as he threw his head back in amusement. Dying to a low chuckle, it glinted brightly in his eyes, teasing and taunting her assertion.

"A minister's daughter from Iowa," he repeated. "Is that supposed to make your claim legitimate? Because you're from Iowa?"

He laughed softly again, infuriating Selena to the point where she almost choked on her own anger. "It happens to be the truth! And I don't give a damn whether you believe me or not!"

His eyes widened in pretended shock. "What would your father say if he heard such language?" he murmured reprovingly.

A frustrated moan was wrenched from her throat. "Why won't you listen to me? I tried to return the money to you."

"I'm sure you did." There was a single trace of disbelief in his voice.

"I did," Selena snapped. "When I discovered it in my purse, I sealed it in an envelope. I was going to slip it under your door when you were out. Don't you remember those phone calls you got where there was nobody on the other end? It was me, calling to see if you were in your room."

"How can you prove that when there was no one on the other end?" Chance continued to bait her, seeming to derive amusement from her anger.

41

"Surely the fact that I know about the phone calls proves something," she retorted.

"It might prove that you were trying to figure out a way to get back into my room to retrieve your dress and shoes," he pointed out.

"I wasn't," Selena denied his claim in an impatient burst. "As a matter of fact, I even tried to leave the money for you at the desk this morning, but you'd already checked out."

"Why didn't you just return it in person instead of supposedly trying all these covert attempts?" His look was bland, unrevealing and unconvinced.

"Are you crazy?" she expelled in a laughing, scornful breath. "And risk ending up like this—in bed with you?" Suddenly aware of their prone position she tried to push away and sit up, but his hand pressed her shoulders to the bed. "I ran out of your hotel room to avoid this!" she hissed.

His gaze narrowed thoughtfully as he weighed her words. "All right," he conceded. "Return my money and I'll forget the whole thing."

Selena paled, the anger flowing out of her with a rush. "I don't have it anymore," she said in a small voice.

She hadn't been aware of any softening in his expression until it hardened. "You don't have it anymore," he repeated her statement. "You had it this morning, but you don't have it now. I suppose I'm wasting my time by asking you what happened to it?"

"The desk clerk wouldn't give me your name or address so I couldn't mail it to you," Selena tried desperately to explain the dilemma she had been in. "And it wasn't mine, so I couldn't keep it."

"Oh, no, a minister's daughter couldn't keep money that didn't rightfully belong to her," he agreed wryly. "So what did you do with it?"

"I gave it away." She couldn't tell whether he was believing any part of what she said. "To a charity."

A smile seemed to play with his mouth, the corners twitching. "Do you expect me to believe that?"

"It's the truth, I swear," Selena vowed.

"It seems to me," he said, pausing to watch his finger as it traced the sensitive cord on the side of her neck, "that we're back to where we started—with the money paid and the goods still to be delivered."

"Will you stop?" Panic bubbled in her throat and she swallowed it down. His mouth descended towards her and she turned her head to elude it. "Don't!"

Winding a bunch of auburn hair around his fingers, Chance tugged her back, capturing her lips with practiced ease. His other hand slid over the bareness of her stomach, arousing a tumult of emotion that she was powerless to control. His seductive mastery was completely beyond her experience.

When he felt her trembling and unwilling response, he lowered his head, seeking the hollow of her throat. Selena's resistance stiffened as she felt the bra strap slipping from her shoulder and the trailing tips of his fingers making their way to the exposed swell of her breast. She clawed at his hand, only to have it closed firmly over the lacy cup of her brassiere.

"Don't do this, please," she repeated an earlier plea. "I'm not that kind of girl."

He followed the curve of her neck to her ear, nuzzling it, his warm breath arousing and stimulating. "Are you trying to convince me that you don't sell your favors despite what I overheard at the café?"

"I don't, no," Selena protested, fighting the breathlessness that had attacked her voice. "Those men thought that was what I did and I just went along with it. It was...It was just a little harmless fun, a joke. When I saw you later at the hotel, I didn't know what to do. One lie just led to another."

He moved, his mouth playing over her lips, teasing and tantalizing them into wanting his kiss. "Isn't that a strange kind of joke for a minister's daughter to be playing?"

"I don't think you've known many minister's children," she breathed tightly. "We tend to be more mischievous than other kids."

A swift, hard kiss effectively silenced her before Chance unexpectedly levered himself from her. Propped up by an elbow, he studied her flushed and shaken expression.

"Suppose I believe that you aren't that kind, what then?" he challenged.

"Do you believe me?" She searched his dark, unreadable features.

"I believe at least part of your story, although I find your tale about what happened to my money is a little hard to swallow," he returned.

"It's true," Selena rushed. "You can look through my bag and see that, apart from some traveler's checks, I only have a little cash."

"That doesn't prove anything. You could have spent it to pay for this cruise." His gaze narrowed. "Unless my aunt paid your passage."

"I paid my own fare," she flashed, resenting his accusation, "with my own money."

"Or was it mine?" Chance taunted softly.

"It wasn't. I told you what I did with your money!"

"I know what you told me." Skepticism was etched in his words. "But there's still the very real possibility that you used it to finance this cruise, investing it in the hope of a larger return."

"What are you talking about?" Selena frowned angrily.

"I'm sure there are several wealthy widowers on board."

"I'm not looking for a husband," she interrupted coldly.

"And my aunt is a trusting, vulnerable woman," he concluded. "She's completely taken in by you. You know that, don't you?"

"I don't think I like what you're implying." Wary, iridescent fires smoldered in her eyes and her auburn hair fanned over the pillow like a flaming crown.

"Not any more than I do," Chance stated. "But if you were planning to con any money out of her, on whatever pretext that red head of yours has dreamed up, you'd better forget it. Because, honey, I'm going to see to it that you don't get a penny."

Selena was indignant. "It was never my intention!"

"As if you would admit that it was," he jeered.

"You disgust me!" Her voice trembled with the violence of her emotions. With a surge of strength, she pushed him away. "Get out of my cabin!"

As she sat up, Chance rolled over onto his back, folding his hands beneath his head. "But, there is still the matter of where I'm going to spend the night, isn't there?" he asked, looking very much at home.

"Well, you certainly aren't going to stay here!" she snapped.

His gaze slid over the single bed and Selena already cramped against the wall. "No, it would be too crowded with both of us, but luckily you have a spare bed that's empty."

"I'd sooner have a snake in my room than you!" Selena hissed, discovering she was treacherously close to tears. "So you can just get out and see if the Barkley name can work any wonders with the captain."

Laughter again rolled from his throat as he swung himself to his feet with an ease unexpected in a man of his size. His hand was in front of him, holding a key.

"What's that?" Selena eyed it warily, almost afraid that he had somehow managed to obtain her cabin key from her purse.

"The key to my cabin," he informed her. "You see—" he was confident now; it was written in every line of his stance "—when I found you sitting with Julia, I arranged for a passage on this cruise so I could keep an eye on you."

"Does Julia know?"

"Not yet. I wanted to find out what your game was first," he answered.

Resentment seethed in Selena. "Julia told me what an important and busy man you are. I suppose I should feel flattered that you canceled everything and came on this cruise because of me," She stiffened as another thought occurred to her. "Or is it entirely because of me?" At his silence, she pursued it. "You want to stop this thing with Leslie, don't you?"

"That's a personal, family matter and none of your business," Chance stated coldly.

"Then I'm right," Selena concluded. "How can you be so heartless? Julia is old enough to make her own decisions. Your family has no right to stand in the way of something that will bring her happiness."

44

"I have no intention of discussing it with you. And I suggest that you stay out of it." There was a deadly calm about him.

"Is that right?" Although intimidated, Selena still defied him.

"Yes." His gaze glittered over her, implying amusement at her challenge. "Put some clothes on. Unless you intend to go to dinner like that?"

"I'll get dressed—" she paused pointedly, her lips tightening "—when you leave."

"You're only going to be putting clothes over what I've already seen." His eyes were crinkled, laughing at her again. "Is this what you're planning to wear?" Turning, he nodded to the pink-flowered dress laid out on the other bed.

"It is," Selena acknowledged stiffly.

"Very pretty." Chance picked it up, fingering the synthetic material. "Although it isn't nearly as sexy as the red one." He tossed it to her. "Put it on."

Glaring at him, Selena had the distinct impression that if she refused, he was quite capable of taking a hand in it himself. This was one time, she decided, when discretion was the better part of valor. Clutching her robe tightly shut and holding the dress in front of her for added protection, she slid from the bed and retreated behind the closed door of the bathroom.

When she emerged from the bathroom several minutes later, fully clothed and with fresh makeup, Chance was standing at the window. He turned, running a practiced eye over her.

"It took you long enough," he observed, but without complaining.

"I had trouble with the zipper," Selena admitted, smoothing the obi sash at the waistline.

The dress was superbly and simply styled, from its slender band neck with its demure front slash to the artful seaming curving the material over her torso and sweeping to a full skirt. The delicately flowered print was in the softest pinks imaginable, flattering the copper tint of her hair.

"I could have given you a hand with the zipper," Chance stated, watching as she slipped her sheer stockinged feet into her shoes.

"It occurred to me, and I rejected the thought just as quickly," she retorted. "Shall we go?" Her purse was in the hand he extended to her.

Holding her tongue was an effort since the urge was strong to tell him where she thought he should go, but wisdom and temperance prevailed. Taking her purse, she walked to the door. As she reached to unlock it, his hand was there to turn the key and push the door open, his arm brushing her shoulder.

Selena stepped quickly over the raised threshold onto the outer deck. Anxious to escape the confining intimacy of the cabin, she nearly walked into the path of two other couples heading for the stairs. Chance's hands were there, curving into the short sleeves covering her upper arms and pulling her back, and she tensed under his hold.

45

One of the men glanced from her to Chance to the cabin door swinging closed. He couldn't possibly know that she and Chance weren't married, but she felt the growing pink of embarrassment warming her cheeks. The boat was not so large that at some point the man would discover they weren't.

As the two couples descended the stairs, Chance released her to move from behind Selena to her side. She averted her head, but not quickly enough to escape his observant gaze. She tried to hurry to the stairs, but his hand gripped her elbow to forestall her rush.

"Are you blushing?" he questioned, tipping his head down for a closer inspection.

"Yes," she muttered the admission under her breath.

"Why?" Chance sounded amused.

"Because I don't like the idea of those people seeing you come out of my cabin," she retorted. "They might get the wrong idea."

"Just as long as they believe that you're with me, I don't particularly care what other ideas they get," Chance stated.

"Well, I'm not with you!" Selena flashed.

"For the duration of this cruise, everyone is going to think you are," he informed her. "Because I'm going to keep you in my sight every waking minute."

"Is that right?" Her chin lifted in the beginnings of defiance.

His mouth curved into a smile, one that didn't reach his eyes as she knew it could if it was genuine. "I suggest that you be glad I said every *waking* minute."

"If that's supposed to be a threat, I'm not frightened," she countered.

"Suit yourself," Chance shrugged, and released her elbow. "But you'd do well to remember all that I've said."

Selena turned up her nose at his advice and walked to the stairs, well aware that he was following her. And she was also aware that there was very little she could do about it, short of pushing him overboard, and she didn't have the strength for that.

Not until she had reached the cabin deck did Selena realized that she had no idea where the meals were served. She glanced around, hoping to see fellow passengers on their way to dinner so that she might follow them. There wasn't a soul in sight.

It grated to have to turn to Chance. "Do you know where the Orleans Room is located?" she requested stiffly.

Slashing grooves were etched from nose to mouth on each side of his tanned face. They deepened now as his mouth tightened to conceal a smile. He knew how it irritated Selena to ask his assistance and was complacently amused.

"I believe I do, yes," he drawled, and guided her to the area where the forward cabin lounge was located.

46

As Selena entered the lounge ahead of Chance, Julia saw her. "I was wondering where you were, Selena," she exclaimed. "I was about to go down without you." Then she saw the man following Selena. "Chance! What are you doing here?" Julia greeted him with surprise and delight, with none of the trepidation she had voiced at his appearance before the boat left the dock.

"I decided to come on the cruise with you," was his brief reply. He nodded to Selena adding, "I found...Selena." He paused deliberately before using her given name while his gaze flicked to her red hair, reminding Selena of his nickname for her. "She was wandering about lost and I volunteered to show her where the dining room was."

"Oh, dear," Julia exclaimed in dismay. "I didn't tell you where it was located, did I?"

"It's all right," Selena assured her.

"Thank you, Chance, for directing her here," Julia smiled at her nephew, then sighed happily. "I'm so glad you've come, Chance." She clasped one of his hands warmly between her own. "I so wanted a member of my family at the wedding and now you're here."

"Yes, I'm here," Chance agreed blandly.

But Selena noticed the way his jaw had hardened when Julia had referred to her marriage to Leslie. She knew intuitively that if Chance had his way, the marriage would never take place. Obviously he was going to do everything in his power to stop it. Selena resented, on Julia's behalf, this desire to dominate.

5

"Shall we go down to dinner?" Chance suggested, distracting the conversation from Julia's elopement.

Behind the grand staircase was a stairwell leading below. The identifying words Orleans Room were in open view. At the base of the stairs, double doors of cream white stood open in welcome, the head waiter standing just inside, resplendent and distinguished in an excellently cut black suit, and smiling a greeting as the trio descended the stairs.

"You and your companion have table 40 as usual, Miss Julia," the man announced with grave courtesy, before turning to Chance. "And your table, sir?"

From his suit pocket, Chance withdrew a round, numbered disc indicating table 83. He handed it to the maître d'.

Selena darted Chance a look through sweeping lashes. He caught and read the message written in her eyes, triumphant relief that she wouldn't have to suffer his presence at the dinner table.

"Your table is on the starboard side sir," the head waiter explained. "Your waiter will show you."

"This is my nephew, André," Julia spoke up. "Chance Barkley."

48

"Mr. Barkley," the man bowed slightly as he shook Chance's hand. "It's a pleasure to have you aboard." Then, to all three of them, he said, "Enjoy the buffet."

The tables of food ran the length of the room down its center, splitting the dining area in half. Most of the passengers had already helped themselves and were seated at their assigned tables. Filing behind Julia, Selena noted the spaciousness of the room. There was no suggestion of crowding, and the leisurely atmosphere invited her to take her time over the varied selection of salads, vegetables and entrées.

Their waiter was at the end of the buffet to carry their plates to the table for four. An elderly couple were already occupying two of the chairs, and there was a friendly round of introductions as Selena and Julia joined them.

Selena couldn't remember the last time she had enjoyed such an unhurried meal. Against the middle of the far wall was a bandstand, complete with a grand piano. A man sat at the keyboard, softly playing a medley of show tunes. Her gaze wandered to the opposite side of the room and glimpsed the satin blackness of the back of Chance's head, but he was too far away to disturb her serenity.

Their waiter, another college-aged boy, appeared unobtrusively at the table, refilling Selena's coffee cup and whisking away her dessert plate. Selena relaxed in her chair to listen to the dreamily soothing piano music.

The arrival of night had darkened the windows. Water shimmered occasionally beyond the panes where the lights from the steamboat touched the river's surface.

Yet the sun-yellow walls of the dining room kept the mood mellow, enhanced by the glow of Tiffany lamps located on the walls between each of the green shuttered windows. The individual lights resembled a trio of palm fronds, their stalks secured with a gold bow, while crystal pendants were suspended from the tip of each golden spiked leaflet.

The hoarse whistle of the steamboat blasted a single, long wail. In the distance came a long, answering toot, low and deep, reverberating into the interior of the boat. Curious, Selena waited expectantly for something to happen. Julia noticed her expression and smiled.

"Our captain just signaled to another vessel coming down river that we would pass on the port side," she explained. "The other vessel, probably a towboat with barges, returned the signal. Two whistles would mean the starboard side."

"I see," Selena said, nodding her understanding.

"It's written on the walls by the door," Julia pointed.

Selena turned slightly in her chair. On the wall to the left of the double doors was written "One whistle port." On the right it read, "Two whistles starb'rd." The sign also signified which side was which.

49

"The vessel will be going by shortly," Julia added. "Would you like to go up for a better view?"

"If you're ready?" Selena agreed with qualification. The other couple at their table had already left.

"I am," the older woman acknowledged, folding her linen napkin and placing it on the table near her coffee cup.

It was cool outside and Selena chose to watch the massed barges and pushing towboat go past from the shelter of the forward cabin lounge. She had seen similar barges and towboats from the New Orleans dock, but it was a much more impressive sight from the interior of the moving steamboat as the two vessels met and glided slowly and silently past one another.

When the towboat was gone, there was only shadowing darkness outside the window. Selena turned away and found Chance standing behind her, smoke curling from the slender cigar between his fingers.

"You'll get used to it." His perceptive eyes had noticed the bemused look that hadn't completely left her face and recognized its cause. "In a few days, you won't even glance out the window when the pilot blows the whistle."

Selena didn't respond to his cynical observation, but she hoped he was wrong. Instead she remarked, "I hope you enjoyed your meal."

"I did. Did you?"

Selena managed only a nod before Julia broke in to ask, "Chance, do you recall what time the show in the Orleans Room is this evening?"

"Nine-fifteen, I believe," he answered.

"You are going, aren't you?" Julia directed the question to her nephew.

"I thought I would, yes,"

"It should be very good," Julia remarked idly. "They have some excellent entertainers aboard. I know you'll enjoy it, Selena."

"Oh, but I'm not going." She had made up her mind the instant that she heard that Chance Barkley was.

"But it's your first night," Julia protested, while Chance smiled knowingly.

"Yes, I know, but it's been a full day and I want to write to my parents. I haven't let them know yet about my change of plans." Selena felt her excuse was excellent, even if Chance did guess why she was making it. "There'll be other nights and other shows."

"I suppose so," Julia conceded gracefully.

"Excuse me. I noticed the gift shop was opened and I'd like to pick up a few postcards." She was already moving away, making her escape while she could. "I'll see you in the morning, Julia. Good night."

There was an interesting assortment of souvenirs displayed on the gift-shop counter, but Selena didn't take the time to look at them. She purchased a few cards to send to friends at home and left.

An hour later, the letter to her parents was written—to fulfill the excuse she had made—as well as one to her girl friend Robin. Selena glanced at the turned-down covers of the bed, courtesy of a dinner-time visit by the maid, and knew she wasn't ready yet to sleep.

She hesitated, then took a white crocheted shawl from the chest of drawers and the cabin key from her handbag. Wrapping the shawl around her shoulders, she stepped out of the door onto the outer deck. At first, she was struck by the silence of the night, broken only by the rush of water cascading from the paddle wheel and the muffled throb of the engines.

Moving to the railings, she leaned against the teakwood handrail and stared at the glow of light from New Orleans. Rising above it was a big, full moon, looking like a fat Georgia peach. Selena corrected the thought, deciding it was more salmon-colored, but breathtaking just the same.

"It's beautiful," she murmured aloud.

"Yes, it is."

Selena turned with a start as Chance separated himself from the shadows and moved to the railing. "Why don't you quit spying on me?" she demanded and pivoted back to stare at the river.

Chance ignored her question, seeming to indicate that he didn't believe it warranted an answer, and remarked, "You didn't mention that you were going to take a romantic stroll around the deck."

"I just wanted some fresh air before I turned in," she replied, and immediately wished she hadn't offered an explanation. It was none of his business. "What are you doing out here? I thought you were going to the show." Her sideways glance found him negligently leaning a hip against the railing to face her profile.

"I wanted some fresh air." He used her excuse deliberately, Selena thought, to mock her somehow.

"Go and find it somewhere else," she retorted, her nerves stretching thin like a piano wire.

"Have any suggestions?" Chance sounded amused.

Selena felt an unreasoning irritation, a desire to lash out, to claw. "Why don't you try the bottom of the river?"

Silence followed. In the stillness she had an inexplicable urge to retract her words, to make peace whatever the cost.

When Chance did speak, it was in a voice that reminded her of velvet. "Do you really want to be on deck alone—under that moon?" Her gaze slid to the full moon, bathing her with the serenity of its light and catching her in its romantic spell. "It seems to say, 'for lovers only', doesn't it?" His voice sounded dangerously close.

When Selena turned, she turned into him. Her hands, clutching the crossed ends of the shawl, brushed against his jacket. The moonlight was masking his compelling features in glistening bronze, but his eyes, black midnight pools, fathomless and shimmering, were focused on her lips. Everything seemed to come to a standstill, her heart, her breath, her thoughts.

His hands settled lightly on her shoulders as his head bent lower. She knew what he was going to do, but Chance had kissed her so many times before, it seemed natural. At the warm touch of his mouth she responded, hesitantly at first, then with increasing ease. She let his shaping hands mold her to him, his oak-strong solidness something she could lean on.

The pressure of his kiss relaxed, although his firm, male lips continued sensually playing with hers, their warm breath mingling. "I've wanted you, Red, ever since I saw you again at the hotel," Chance murmured against her mouth.

The use of her nickname set off the alarm bell, making her aware of the danger in his embrace. This was not an innocently romantic kiss in the moonlight, not with Chance Barkley as a participant. Why had she let herself be caught up in all the talk about the moon and lovers?

She twisted out of his arms. "You're still making the same mistake about me," she accused with a painful catch in her voice.

His head was drawn back, a hint of arrogance in his look. "Am I?"

"Yes, you are." Chance made no effort to stop her as she stepped away, aware that in her weakness and foolishness she had given him cause to think that way. "I'm going to my cabin," she announced, adding a definite "alone" when he started to follow her.

His mouth quirked. "A gentleman always sees a lady to her door."

"You aren't a gentleman," Selena retorted.

His eyes said, "You aren't a lady," but they had already crossed the few feet to her cabin. Selena tried to ignore him as she inserted the key into the lock. When she started to pull the door open, his hand was there to stop it.

"Don't you think I should check to make sure there aren't any unwanted visitors in your room?" he queried mockingly.

"Such as?" she asked in caustic challenge.

"Spiders, mice, the odd creatures that might have slipped aboard."

"Like rats," Selena suggested with a cloyingly sweet smile, and ducked under his arm to slip inside the door.

She heard his soft chuckles as she closed it behind her. She waited just inside until she heard his footsteps moving away from her cabin.

After changing into her nightclothes, she switched off the light and crawled between the covers of her bed. A couple walked by her door, passengers murmuring a greeting to someone. There was a tightness in her chest as she heard Chance's familiar voice respond.

He was still outside her cabin, somewhere close. She rolled onto her side, punching her pillow with the unladylike wish that it was his face. But that wasn't really what she wished and she knew it.

Morning brought renewed zest and a firm resolve that she wasn't going to let Chance Barkley get under her skin—or anywhere else!

Her clothing was casual for the day of cruising up the river. The loose-fitting sweater top was a natural shade with toast and black stripes ringing the bodice, the hips and the hem, the short sleeves cuffed at the elbow with more stripes. Natural linen pants matched the top, and a black and tan plaid scarf secured her hair at the back of her neck, the silk material brushing the skin left bare by the boat neckline of the sweater.

Breakfast was being served in the Orleans Room, and Selena skipped lightly down the stairs, the brilliant sunlight shining outside reflected in her bright, carefree spirits.

Inside the dining-room entrance, she stopped dead. Chance was sitting at her table, sipping a cup of coffee. When he saw her poised inside the doorway, he rose and pulled out a chair for her with mock courtesy.

Numbly Selena moved to the table, her resolve vanishing in a rush of irritation. "What are you doing here?" she demanded.

He continued to stand beside the chair, waiting for her to be seated. "I arranged to have my table changed," he explained with a wicked glint in his eyes. "The head waiter quite understood that I would prefer to sit with my aunt."

She wanted to turn and stalk from the room, but that would give him too much satisfaction. She ignored the chair he held out for her and chose one that seated her opposite him.

The long, narrow menu card was leaning against the crystal vase of carnations in the center of the table. Selena picked it up and forced herself to concentrate on the selections, ignoring Chance as he took his chair.

"Are you ready to order?" Dick, their waiter, asked as he appeared at the table.

"Selena?" Chance directed the inquiry to her,

"I haven't quite decided. You go ahead."

He hesitated, then ordered a full breakfast. The waiter turned to Selena. "Have you made up your mind, miss?"

"I think I'll just have orange juice and a sweet roll," she stated, replacing the menu. "And coffee."

When the waiter left for the kitchen, Selena felt Chance's gaze center on her. "I expected an Iowa girl like you would eat a hearty breakfast," he commented.

"Did you?" Coolly, Selena lifted her gaze to meet his. "But then you've consistently misjudged me, haven't you?"

Chance made no reply, his gaze narrowing briefly. Silence reigned through the morning meal with Selena naturally finishing first and excusing herself from the table to leave him there alone.

Later she saw him on deck, but he made no attempt to approach her, although she noticed, with irritation, that he kept her in sight. Soon his presence lost the ability to chafe as she became caught up in the spell of the Mississippi River.

The *Delta Queen* steamed up the river with majestic slowness, a stately, old-fashioned lady taking a leisurely paddle up the Mississippi. Levees, emerald green with thick grasses, paralleled the river's winding course as it sometimes seemed to attempt to twist back into itself.

Trees forested the banks. Cottonwoods, cypress, sycamores—an almost endless variety—grew there to baffle and break up the raging current when the river went out of its banks at flood stage. Through breaks in the trees, there were glimpses over the levees of sprawling flatlands, cotton and sugar plantations.

A trio of egrets was perched on a fallen tree near the river's edge, and a deer grazing in a grassy glade flicked his white tail before bounding into the trees. The river itself was a dirty brown, rushing full between its banks, creating eddies and then destroying them. Logs and tree branches were swept helplessly in its current, along with a million spring seeds. The river was showing a face that had changed little since the days when steamboats ruled its waters and Mark Twain described its lure.

But there were other faces; buoys marked the channel and industry spilled onto its banks. Vast chemical plants and refineries with their complex network of intertwining pipes and towering stacks rose above the levees. Water towers and church steeples marked towns that were hidden from view.

Except for the Crescent City of New Orleans, nowhere did the modern face become more evident than at Baton Rouge. The highrise buildings of the city proper marked its center. On either side of the river loading terminals lined the banks with oceangoing ships of every description. Some were being unloaded and giant cranes were loading others. Selena left her comfortable deck chair to walk to the railing for a better look.

"Baton Rouge is the farthest inland, major port in the States," said Chance, appearing at her side.

Selena found the scene all too fascinating to object to his presence. "It's an impressive array of ships, but why are they all flying the American flag? Surely they can't all be American ships?"

"It's a courtesy to fly the flag of the port nation. The flag of the ship's country is on the stern," he explained.

"I see," she nodded. "There's one from Holland," she pointed.

54

"The next one is from Glasgow, Scotland, where the *Delta Queen* was made." Selena faced him in surprise. "The *Delta Queen* was made in Scotland?" she repeated. "I didn't know that."

"Yes, the steelwork for her and the *Delta King* was fabricated in Glasgow and temporarily assembled on the River Clyde. The parts were all marked, then torn down and shipped to California where she was reassembled and finished. But it was the same shipbuilding center in Scotland where the *Queen Mary* was fitted out that this riverboat had her start," he concluded.

"Amazing!" she breathed, and looked back at the freighter from Scotland. Several crew members had gathered on the bridge of the freighter to watch the *Delta Queen* steam by, her paddle wheel churning tan foam. One of the crew was taking pictures of the riverboat and Selena wondered if he knew of the *Delta Queen's* beginnings in his homeland. Or did she just seem an anachronism gliding slowly past the sleek, ultramodern tankers and freighters?

"When was she built?" Selena questioned absently.

"In the mid-1920s I think. She carried passengers on the Sacramento River back and forth from San Francisco to Sacramento, California."

"Yes, I remember the couple at our dinner table last night mentioned that one of their older relations had been on the *Delta Queen* when she was in California many years ago," she nodded.

The breeze had picked up, whipping around the stern. It tugged a strand of hair free of Selena's scarf and laid it across her cheek. Before she could push it aside, Chance's hand was there, smoothing it behind her ear and making her conscious of him.

He was tall and vital, his dark eyes glinting with an inner light. With the breeze ruffling the thick crispness of his black hair, he looked rugged and manly, totally in command. His silk print shirt was plastered to his torso by the wind, the material alternately clinging and billowing to enhance his muscular physique.

The cuffs of his shirt sleeves were rolled up twice to reveal a portion of the rippling muscles in his forearms. The top two buttons of the shirt were unfastened, exposing his throat and the tanned column of his neck. Chance Barkley was a handsome brute, a black-haired devil, and the heady sight of him shook her senses.

She tore her gaze away from him, suddenly finding it very essential to speak and break the silence. "The *Delta Queen* has a very interesting history, doesn't she?" Her voice was much steadier than she had expected and she could feel her pulse settling into a more even rhythm.

"Yes, it has," Chance agreed.

Another couple moved to the railing near them, an older man and his wife. After several minutes, the man struck up a conversation with Chance and

55

Selena drifted away to reclaim her deck chair and watch the outskirts of Baton Rouge slip by.

She hadn't been there long when Julia stopped, saying, "Good morning, Selena. Are you going to take your 'eleven at eleven'?"

"I beg your pardon?" Selena blinked.

Julia laughed softly, "Eleven laps around the sundeck—which is a mile—at eleven o'clock, with the calliope providing the marching music."

"I don't think so," she said, smiling wryly at her own lassitude. "I feel too lazy." Overhearing their conversation, Chance caught her eye, a mocking reminder in his that an Iowa girl should be more industrious. Selena ignored the look with an effort.

"Are you going, Julia?"

"Oh, yes. I have so much energy I must channel it somewhere," she declared, and moved toward the stairs. "See you at lunch."

Watching her leave, Selena knew that the bright sparkle in Julia's eyes came from more than just energy. She was sure it was born of excitement because the next day they would be arriving in Natchez, where Leslie was waiting for her.

Selena felt a pang of envy, hoping that some day she might have that special glow the older woman possessed. Almost of its own volition, her gaze swung to Chance, leaning backward against the railing, his arms crossed in front of him.

Something jolted through her as she found him watching her, but the emotion was fleeting and indefinable, and Chance's attention was soon claimed by the man standing beside him.

The sensation didn't return. In the afternoon Selena attended a lecture on the *Delta Queen's* history. Julia didn't go because she had heard it all before. Neither did Chance, and Selena guessed that he was equally well informed on the subject.

His sketchy outline had whetted her appetite to hear more and she was not disappointed by the lecture. Mike, the cruise director, spoke of her construction and the almost one million dollars that had been spent to build the *Delta Queen*, a phenomenal sum to pay for a riverboat in the 1920s. He told of her life on the Sacramento River in California and the years that she had been laid up when the Depression hit.

During World War II the U.S. Navy took over the *Delta Queen*, using her as a troop carrier in San Francisco Bay, ferrying soldiers to and from ocean vessels. With the navy's predilection for battleship gray, every inch of her was painted—including the stained glass panels set with copper, which were set in the top of the windows in the lounges on both the cabin deck and the texas deck.

After the war the *Delta Queen* was auctioned off, sold to the Green Line that was already operating overnight passenger trips on the Mississippi

River. It was then that she was shored and crated like a huge piano in a box, and towed down the Pacific Coastline, through the Panama Canal into the Gulf of Mexico to the Mississippi River. This riverboat was not designed for the ocean or its fury, yet the *Delta Queen* had made it intact, to the stunned amazement of many an ocean man who had predicted her doom on the high seas.

The story of the Congressional battle to keep her from being banned forever from traveling the western rivers was recounted, along with the tale of the ultimate, though possibly temporary success. Finally, the cruise director told of the recent construction of her sister ship, the *Mississippi Queen*, a sleek modern paddle-wheel steamboat with a personality all her own.

Selena came away from the lecture with a new appreciation for the riverboat and the feeling that she had only heard the highlights, that there was much of the *Delta Queen's* rich history she didn't know.

At dinner that evening it was their scheduled arrival at Natchez the following day that indirectly dominated the conversation—at least between Julia and Selena. The older woman talked about her anticipation of being with Leslie and reminisced about their previous times together.

Chance was almost grimly silent. As far as Selena was concerned, his dislike of Leslie and his disapproval of the coming marriage was practically a tangible thing. She considered his attitude autocratic and insensitive.

"I've decided to buy a new dress in Natchez for my wedding," Julia announced. "But I can't make up my mind what color. I think it would be in bad taste for a woman my age to wear white, even though I've never been married before. I was considering something in cream or beige or perhaps yellow. Leslie always said yellow was my color."

Selena was about to comment when Chance broke in curtly, "Julia, you're boring Selena with all this nonsense about your wedding."

"That's absurb!" Selena flared, her spoon poised above the peach melba. "What woman would find wedding plans boring? And personally I find it reassuring that a woman of Julia's age can love as deeply and as romantically as a younger person."

She observed the hardening of his features at her quick and vigorous defense of Julia and turned away, fixing a determinedly interested look on her face as she glanced at the older woman.

"With your hair, I think something in silver gray might be very complimentary," she suggested, noting the silver wings at the temples of Julia's otherwise dark hair.

Julia hesitated for a second, glancing apprehensively at her nephew before picking up the conversation where Selena had left off, and Chance's disapproving silence was ignored. But a strained atmosphere remained.

57

It wasn't relieved until the three returned to the New Orleans Room after dinner for the banjo concert. The room had been transformed into a night-club with tables—minus their linen and silverware—chairs, the lights dimmed, and drinks being served from the Mark Twain Saloon.

The banjo player sat on a stool in front of the band. Mustached, with brown, waving hair, he wore black pants, a white shirt and red vest with garters around his sleeves.

He introduced himself in a drawling voice and said, "You all have come here tonight to hear a banjo concert. That's good, 'cause that's what we got planned." He plunked a few strings and looked out at the audience. "Banjos and riverboats almost seem synonymous. You think of one, then the other." A shyly mischievous smile curved his mouth. "Course, you all know that the banjo is the only musical instrument invented in America and you are about to find out why we're the only country that had the nerve." With that, he immediately broke into a rousing version of "Waiting for the Robert E. Lee."

Before the song was over, everyone in the room was clapping along, and Selena felt the tension leave her, extinguished by the gay, infectious spirit of the music.

After the concert Julia left, insisting it was time for her to retire with all the things happening the next day. Selena lingered to sample the late-night snacks, as did Chance. Somewhere along the way, they were separated as Selena paused to chat with some of her fellow passengers.

When the band began playing some dance music, she saw Chance at the crew's table in the far corner of the room, talking to the chief purser. He seemed to have forgotten about her, and Selena was positive she was glad about it.

Sipping at her hot chocolate, she watched the older couples on the dance floor, marveling at their grace and ability. When the chocolate was gone, and with it her reason for staying, Selena walked to the stairs.

Before she reached the first step, Chance was at her side.

"I'll walk you to your cabin," he stated.

"There's no need," she balked.

With typical arrogance, he ignored her protest and pressed a hand against the small of her back to guide her up the stairs. She submitted to his lead, however ungraciously, and they walked in silence up the stairs through the forward cabin lounge to the outer deck.

Ripples of moonlight danced over the river and the cobweb silhouettes of trees along the banks. A corner of the full moon was lopped off, making it look like a chipped silver dollar in a velvet sky. The stars were big and bright, so close Selena felt she could reach out and touch them. It was a warm and languid southern night with a moist breeze stirring the air.

"Don't you think this charade has gone far enough?" Chance issued the demanding question in a cold, hard voice that shattered the evening's mood.

Selena's eyes widened, partly in anger and partly in fear that they were back to the question of her profession. "What are you talking about?"

"I'm referring to the way you keep humoring Julia, of course," he snapped, impatient with her obtuseness.

"Humoring her?" she repeated, her resentment at his attitude at dinner returning to fuel her anger. "I am not humoring her! I'm glad she's found someone to love. And you should be, too, instead of trying to spoil her happiness. She's a warm, wonderful person. She doesn't deserve to have a family like yours!"

She didn't flinch under his piercing regard, his eyes narrowing to black slits as he searched deep into her soul as if testing the sincerity of her words. Turning, he said nothing in defense but merely escorted her up the stairs to the texas deck and her cabin.

He left her at the door with a brusque good-night, which, still simmering from their exchange, Selena didn't bother to return. As she closed her door she saw he had moved to the railing.

A lighter flamed in his hand. He cupped it to the slender cigar in his mouth, the lighter briefly illuminating his features and revealing an expression of grim thoughtfulness.

As Selena got ready for bed, the humid breeze carried the aromatic smoke from his cigar through her open cabin window. The scent lingered long after she had fallen asleep.

6

Selena awakened fairly early the next morning. The river was shrouded in fog when she stepped from her cabin. It seemed a white world with the sky paled to a pearl gray. Even the sun was a white glare in the east. The damp coolness seeped through her sweater to chill her skin, making her hurry down the stairs to the forward cabin lounge.

The first person she saw as she entered the lounge was Chance. He was standing at one of the windows and staring out, and as if sensing her presence, he shot her a glance. An impassive mask had been drawn over his compelling features, making his thoughts unreadable.

Then Selena noticed Julia, looking dejected sitting in one of the chairs. Selena's mouth tightened; she was certain that in some way Chance was to blame for his aunt's expression. She walked directly to the older woman to offer moral support and perhaps undo whatever damage Chance had done.

"Good morning, Julia," she greeted the woman quietly.

Looking up in surprise, Julia recovered to respond, "Oh, good morning Selena." But it was an absent greeting, her thoughts were obviously far away.

"Is something wrong, Julia?" Selena probed gently.

"The chief purser just brought me this message," was the sigh.

Selena noticed the crumpled slip of paper between Julia's twisting fingers. "From Leslie?" she guessed.

"Yes, he won't be able to meet me in Natchez." Disappointment, intense and painful, clouded her expression.

"Oh, no!" Selena breathed out, an instant frown of compassion drawing her eyebrows together.

"He said he'd meet me in Vicksburg instead." Julia attempted to fix a reassuring smile on her face, but she couldn't conceal her regret for the postponement.

"What happened?"

"His car broke down," Julia explained. "Something major, I guess, since he says it's going to take a couple of days to fix."

"I'm so sorry," Selena offered, knowing it was poor comfort.

"It's all right. We'll be in Vicksburg tomorrow, and the day after that Leslie will be there, so I don't have long to wait. It's you I feel badly about," she murmured apologetically.

"Me? Whatever for?" Selena exclaimed.

"My dear, I know you didn't book for the tour of Natchez because you expected to meet Leslie in the afternoon. Now it's too late and you're going to miss seeing it altogether," Julia sighed.

"I don't mind, really," she insisted.

"Of course you do," Julia dismissed Selena's protest. "You're on vacation. You should be going places and doing things instead of letting me interfere in your life, boring you with my troubles."

"You're not boring me and you aren't interfering," Selena stated flatly. "You've been listening to Chance too much." She flashed an angry glance in his direction, throwing invisible, flaming daggers at a point between his broad shoulders. "I enjoy your company and I'm excited about your wedding. Don't pay any attention to what he says."

"You're such a good girl." Julia patted her hand, adding, "And you're so good for my ego."

"I'm glad," Selena smiled, her affection for the older woman steadily growing.

"Before you came in the lounge, I was feeling so low. Now—" the other woman shrugged and smiled "—I even think I could eat some breakfast. Will you join me?"

Selena hesitated. "Not right away," There was something else she wanted to do first. "But I'll be down before you're through."

"Very well," Julia agreed, rising from her chair.

Selena waited until Julia had started down the steps to the Orleans Room before she walked to where Chance stood.

His glance and his voice were indifferent. "Good morning."

There were other passengers around the lounge helping themselves to coffee. Selena's mouth tightened into a hard line. She wasn't in the mood to exchange pleasantries.

"Would you come outside with me?" she requested stiffly. "I want to talk to you."

A brow lifted briefly at her request, his flat black gaze making an assessing sweep of her, noting the light of battle in her eyes, before he complied with her request.

The instant they were outside and out of earshot of their fellow passengers, Selena turned on him, her eyes flashing green sparks.

"Was this your doing?" she demanded.

Chance tipped his head slightly to the side. "I'm afraid I don't follow you."

One of the deckhands was polishing the brass kickboards of the stairs leading to the texas deck. Selena lowered her voice so she couldn't be overheard, but that didn't lessen the heat in her tone.

"You follow my meaning all right," she retorted. "I'm talking about the message Julia supposedly received from Leslie, the one saying he wouldn't be able to meet her in Natchez."

"That message," he nodded in understanding, his bland expression not changing.

"Yes, I know about it. What has it to do with me?"

"That's what I want to know," Selena challenged. "What was your part in it?"

"As I recall the message, Leslie had car trouble," Chance remarked with infuriating calm. "I've been on the boat with you ever since we left New Orleans, so I don't see how you could accuse me of possibly tampering with his car. That is what you're suggesting, isn't it?"

"That's presupposing, of course, that Leslie sent the message."

"Meaning, you think I did and signed his name to it?" His gaze sharpened.

"It's possible," she said grimly. "I saw you talking to the chief purser last night. You could have paid him to deliver the message to Julia this morning. I wouldn't put it past you—you're so determined not to let them get married."

"It could happen that way," he admitted. "But your theory has a flaw."

"What's that?" Selena didn't hide her skepticism.

"If I sent the message and not Leslie, then he'll be waiting at the landing when the boat docks in Natchez, won't he?" Chance reasoned smoothly, causing Selena's doubt in her suspicions to flicker across her face. "Unless you're going to accuse me next of sending a message to Leslie from Julia calling off the wedding?"

She hadn't thought of that. "You could have."

"Perhaps. But I didn't. The message Julia received this morning was not sent by me," he said firmly. "Nor did I arrange to have it sent. I guess you'll have to assume it came from Leslie."

He sounded as if he was telling the truth, but Selena wasn't sure if she could believe him. "Maybe," she submitted grudgingly. "But if I ever have proof that you're lying, I'll—" She compressed her lips tightly, unable to think of the words to complete the threat.

"Yes?" Chance drawled the word, his eyes taunting her.

Her anger was now an impotent thing. Pivoting, she stalked to the lounge door and jerked it open. She had her temper under control by the time she joined Julia for breakfast. Chance had already eaten, she learned, so she wasn't forced to endure his company for the morning meal.

Three whistle blasts signaled their arrival in Natchez shortly before noon. Along with many of the other passengers, Selena moved to the starboard railing to watch the tying-up process. There was no indication of a city, just a few scattered, old buildings, mostly wood and a few brick, with a sheer bluff rising behind them. A treed, parklike veldt stretched several hundred yards downstream.

The boom swung the landing platform to the ramp running down into the river. Deckhands jumped off to drag the heavy ropes to the tie pins. Selena glimpsed the historical plaque identifying the location as Natchez-under-the-Hill, once the most wicked hellhole on the river, peopled with thieves, murderers, gamblers, prostitutes and cutthroats. The river had carried away most of the old town, leaving a row of ramshackle buildings as a representative of the town's sordid past.

On top of the bluff was the city of Natchez where the respectable citizens had lived. Selena knew the glory of its history was duly represented by the more than one hundred antebellum houses that had been restored to their previous grandeur. The Natchez Pilgrimage tours were some of the most famous in the country, and she regretted that she wasn't going.

A few curious townspeople had driven to the waterfront to watch the *Delta queen's* arrival. Some sat in their cars, while others, especially those with children, stood on the banks. The arrival of a steamboat was still an event in this river town.

But there was no middle-aged man alone on the landing, searching the faces of the passengers along the railing for a familiar one. Leslie was not there. Even though Selena didn't know what he looked like, she was certain he wasn't there. She sighed with relief, then wondered why. Because Chance hadn't lied to her? Selena shook her head. It couldn't be that.

When the boat was secured, she went ashore, strolling along the worn path in the parklike area. As the trail curved over a knoll, she stopped at the top to lean a shoulder against a tree and stare at the red paddle wheel of the *Delta queen,* framed by two trees.

The flags circling the top deck ruffled in the breeze against an intense blue sky and a warm, golden sun. Two deckhands were in a rowboat at the bow, applying a fresh coat of paint to the hull.

The leaf of a twig tickled her cheek. Unconsciously she pulled it off and fingered the green leaf. She was in an oddly silent and thoughtful mood, and her mind seemed to be blank. Then she saw Chance coming toward her with slow, purposeful strides. She hesitated and finally stayed where she was.

"They're serving lunch. Aren't you coming?" he asked, stopping beside her.

"I'm not hungry." Her voice was low and flat.

"Watching your diet?" he returned with a teasing inflection.

"I'm just not hungry," Selena said, shrugging and looking away. She became aware of the leaf in her hand and released it, watching it spiral to the ground.

"What's bothering you, Red?" His voice changed to a serious tone.

"Nothing." She slipped the tips of her fingers into her pants pocket, indifferent to his searching gaze.

"Something is," Chance insisted.

Irritation flashed at his persistence. "If there was something, would you really care?" she challenged.

He continued his quiet study of her without offering a reply. Finally her gaze fell from his, her annoyance burning itself out.

When Chance did speak, he asked, "Were you considering going into town?"

"I thought I would," admitted Selena.

"It's a long walk up that hill." She shrugged her indifference to his comment. "I've hired a cab. You could come along with me, if you'd like, and we'll have lunch and drive around to some of the plantations," he invited in a calm, unemotional tone.

She was surprised and wary of his offer, certain he had some reason for asking her that he wasn't saying. A thought occurred to her.

"Is this your idea or Julia's?" she wanted to know.

"Do you really care?" Chance countered with mocking coolness.

With a painful jolt, Selena realized that she did. She didn't want Chance to be making this invitation out of a sense of duty prompted by his aunt.

"You haven't said whether you'd like to go," he reminded her.

Selena hesitated, then decided it didn't make any difference why he had asked her. This was her chance to see Natchez and she would be a fool to turn it down.

"I have to get my handbag," she said in the way of an answer.

"The cab is at the landing. I'll wait for you there."

"I won't be long," Selena promised, and started back to the boat.

After lunching at Stanton Hall, Chance arranged with the cab driver to take them by many of the antebellum homes. They stopped at three that were open to the general public and not restricted to private tours, giving Selena an opportunity to see the interior of these gracious homes.

They returned to the boat half an hour before it was scheduled to leave. As they walked onto the gangplank, Chance asked, "How did you like Natchez?"

"I enjoyed it," Selena answered with genuine enthusiasm. "Thank you for taking me."

"Are you going to your cabin now?"

She nodded. "I thought I'd freshen up and change for dinner."

"It isn't required, you know," he commented.

"Yes, I know, but I feel like it," she shrugged as they climbed the stairs to the cabin deck.

As they reached the top of the stairs, Selena turned toward the double doors leading to the outer deck, but Chance stopped. "Meet me in the texas lounge in a half hour for a drink," he suggested.

"All right." Selena was surprised at how quickly she agreed.

When she left her cabin to meet Chance, the boat was just getting under way. As its stern swung away from the river bank so the boat could back away from the landing, the calliope played a farewell concert on the sundeck.

Its music was interrupted by an announcement over the public address system requesting the passengers to move to the stern of the steamboat. The *Delta Queen's* bow was temporarily stuck in the Mississippi mud, and the captain wanted as much weight as possible to the rear of the steamboat.

Obligingly, Selena waited by her cabin, smiling to herself at the simple remedy. Soon the bow was free and the steamboat was reversing into the channel, once again heading upstream.

Chance was waiting for her at a table in the lounge when she walked in, a drink already in front of him. Greg, the bartender she had met the first day aboard, was at the table almost before she sat down.

"What will you have, Selena?" he asked with familiar ease.

Selena felt the speculative look Chance gave her. "I'll have a margarita," she decided.

"Good choice," Greg winked. "I make the best margarita aboard this boat." And he moved away.

"Do you know him?" questioned Chance, in a bland and impersonal tone that was at odds with the look in his eyes.

"I met him the first day," Selena explained somewhat defensively. "It's a very friendly crew."

"Especially around passengers like you," he added dryly.

Her chin lifted as she had the impression of something derogatory in his remark. "What is that supposed to mean?"

"That you're an attractive young woman, as if you didn't already know," he answered.

As much as she tried, Selena couldn't interpret that as a compliment. Chance had been stating what he saw as a fact, not making a personal comment.

Greg returned with her drink. "The word is out that we'll be meeting the *Mississippi Queen* on her way downstream," he said, referring to the *Delta Queen's* new, modern sister ship.

"When?" Selena's interest was immediate.

"Sometime tonight. It will depend how fast we go upstream and how fast she comes downstream," he smiled. "The captain will be in contact with her by radio before we ever see her. He'll make an announcement ahead of time, letting you know when she'll pass. It'll be a sight to see," Greg declared.

"Where is she coming from?" Selena asked.

"Vicksburg, I think."

"That reminds me. What time will we get into Vicksburg tomorrow?"

"Haven't you heard?" Greg looked at her curiously. "We aren't going to stop at Vicksburg this trip."

"What?" She frowned and glanced at Chance who was studying his drink. But Julia was to meet Leslie in Vicksburg, she thought. "Why not?" she demanded of Greg.

"The river is high from all the spring rains and runoffs, which means the current is swifter, and it's going to take us longer to go up," he explained. "And no one wants to risk getting into Louisville late and missing the steamboat race."

"The steamboat race?" Selena repeated, thinking to herself, but what about Julia and Leslie?

"Yeah," he nodded, finding her blankness curious. "The one between us and the *Belle of Louisville*. We won it last year, and nobody wants to give up the golden antlers, especially by default." A passenger at another table called to him for a round of drinks. Greg excused himself and returned to the bar.

Selena darted an accusing look at Chance. "Did you know we weren't stopping at Vicksburg?"

Impassively he met her gaze. "I heard about it the other day."

"And you didn't say anything to Julia? You know as well as I do that she's planning to meet Leslie in Vicksburg!" She was angered by his indifference.

"She'll find out about it soon enough, if she hasn't already."

"And you didn't see fit to warn her this morning when she was suppressing her disappointment with the knowledge she'd be meeting him in Vicksburg?"

"No, I didn't," Chance admitted without a flicker of remorse.

66

"I don't know whether you don't have a heart or if you're just naturally cruel," Selena declared, almost choking with the effort to keep her temper in check.

He seemed unmoved by her caustic description of him. Lifting his glass to his mouth, he said, "Memphis is our next scheduled stop. I imagine Julia will plan to meet him there."

"Unless you can find a way to prevent it," she added bitterly, and rose from her chair. "You can keep your drink. I'm not interested."

Chance made no attempt to stop her as she walked swiftly from the room. As she neared the grand staircase, she overheard a low comment from one of the passengers, "A lovers' quarrel." It only made her more anxious to leave the room.

At dinner that evening Selena pointedly ignored Chance, her dislike of his heartless ways feeding on itself. It made the meal miserable, turning delicious food into tasteless mush. Julia gave no indication that she was aware they wouldn't be stopping at Vicksburg. She didn't mention either Vicksburg or Leslie at the table. Her conversation was centered on Natchez and the sights that Selena had seen.

The gift shop in the forward cabin lounge was open when Selena left the dining room. She spent some time looking over its items, then wandered up the grand staircase and out through the double doors of the texas. Lounge to the outer deck.

It was a warm, languid night with a three-quarter moon slipping out from behind a cloud. Selena leaned against the railing and gazed out at the shapeless black shadows darkening the banks, trying to convince herself that she was content with her own company.

At eight-thirty the announcement came that the *Mississippi Queen* would be passing them in fifteen minutes on the port side. Selena walked to the left side of the boat to sit in one of the wrought-iron chairs near the fan-shaped air duct. She was soon joined on deck by other passengers, invisible excitement building as the time approached.

Someone said, "There she is, dead ahead."

And a crew member groaned, "Don't put it that way!"

Selena leaned forward to look over the railing and saw the big steamboat coming around the river's bend. She caught her breath at the sight of it. All the decks were ablaze with light, like a tiered birthday cake with all the candles lit in a darkened room.

In the clear night air came the vociferous music from the *Mississippi Queen's* calliope. A murmur ran through the passengers as they recognize the tune, "Cruising down the River."

A spotlight was shining—from the *Delta Queen*, playing over the water ahead of her. The rasping whistle was blown once to officially signal to the

Mississippi Queen that they would pass on the port side and her whistle blasted once in agreement.

As the large paddle wheel steamboat drew steadily closer, one of the bartenders crowded into the railing beside Selena, a flashlight in his hand. He smiled a quick apology, then began flashing the light at the approaching vessel. She caught the answering flash from the forward deck of the *Mississippi Queen*.

The bartender let out a short whoop of delight and began flashing in earnest. "That's my brother," he said, offering Selena a quick explanation. "He works on the *Mississippi Queen*. This is about the only time we see each other."

The bows of the two boats were nearly even now, spotlights roaming over each other's decks. The passengers of the *Mississippi Queen* were all gathered on the outer decks, too, and they shouted in unison, "Hello!" Automatically, Selena heard herself and the others respond with the same greeting. Everyone was waving. It seemed the thing to do.

Slowly the two sister ships glided by each other, the *Mississippi Queen* floating along in the current, her red paddle wheel motionless to prolong the moment of meeting. Then she was past, and her paddle wheel reluctantly began churning the river water again.

Selena leaned back in her chair as the other passengers began leaving the railing. The night was once again ink black, the moon and stars unable to match the brilliant lights of the *Mississippi Queen*.

"Here." A white cloth was offered to her.

Selena glanced up at the donor in surprise. It was Chance, smiling gently as he looked down at her. She was about to protest that she had no need for a handkerchief when she realized that her throat was tight, gripped by the craziest mixture of nostalgia and happiness and the magical beauty of the event. What was more surprising were the welling tears in her eyes.

"Thank you," she muttered, and took the handkerchief to dab her eyes. Laughing, with an emotional catch in the sound, she declared, "I don't know what's the matter with me!"

"I'd say you're turning into a steamboater."

"What's that?" Selena asked, too unnerved by her reaction to remember that she was supposed to dislike Chance actively.

"That's a person who loves steamboats," he answered, taking the handkerchief she returned to him and stuffing it back in his jacket pocket. "Do you feel like a stroll around deck?"

"Yes, I think so." The lump in her throat was beginning to ease as she rose to walk with Chance.

A companionable silence lay between them, his arm curved lightly and impersonally along the back of her waist. Their circuitous route eventual-

68

ly brought them to the stern of the boat near Selena's cabin. In silent unison, they paused at the rear railing to gaze at the waterfall created by the spotlighted paddle wheel.

Other passengers, too, were strolling the decks, exchanging quiet greetings as they passed Selena and Chance. However, one man stopped when he saw them, smiling broadly.

"I see the two of you finally made up after your little tiff this afternoon," he commented, and walked on just as Selena recognized him as being the man she had overheard remarking about their "lovers' quarrel."

Stiffening under the light pressure of Chance's hand, she gave him an odd look. "Why didn't you correct him?"

"What was the point?" he shrugged.

"He thinks we're..."

"Lovers?" supplied Chance, his mouth quirking in mockery at her hesitation over the word.

"Yes," Selena clipped out the answer.

"It's only natural. What do you expect the other passengers to think when they see us together almost constantly?"

"Maybe if you quit following me around all the time, they wouldn't get the wrong impression," she retorted. "And stop hanging around outside my cabin at night!"

"Outside your cabin?" he repeated, a dark brow arching.

"Yes, my cabin," she repeated.

"It just so happens, Red, that I'm hanging around outside my own cabin."

"Your cabin? Where's your cabin?" She demanded in disbelief.

"Number 239, the one right beside yours," he said with a complacent light in his eyes.

"You're lying," Selena accused.

Chance reached into his pocket. "Would you like to see my key?"

She believed him. "No, I wouldn't."

"Which bed do you sleep in?" he asked. "The one on the right as you walk into your cabin?"

"I don't see that it's any of your business, but yes, that's the one," she retorted, still trying to recover from the shock that he had the cabin next to hers.

"We're sleeping side by side with only a wall between us. It's a pity the wall isn't removable," Chance commented in a low voice. "Then I could start collecting on that promise you made in my hotel room."

"I didn't make any promise." She twisted away from the hand on her back. "I keep telling you that, but you refuse to listen. So, from now on, you can just stay away from me."

As she turned away, he caught at her hand. "Where are you going?"

69

"To my cabin." She slipped out of his grasp. "Good night."

"Selena, one word of caution," he followed her to the door. "Don't start sleeping in the other bed or the maid will get suspicious and think someone else is sleeping in your room. And you know how fast rumors spread on this boat!"

Inserting the key in the lock, she jerked her cabin door open and slammed it in his face. But it didn't shut out his remark. When she crawled into bed that night, it was the one she had always slept in.

7

hortly after sunrise Selena stepped out of her cabin, unable to sleep, and tiptoed by Chance's. The chill of the night was still in the strong breeze whipping around the stern. She buttoned the last two buttons of her jacket and tucked her hands in its pockets.

Streamers of scarlet pink trailed across the eastern horizon and the sun was a heavy orange ball. Bluffs rose high along the river banks, the water's course a twisting nest of oxbows.

She wandered around the empty deck and descended the stairs near the bow to the cabin deck. A coffee urn was in the forward cabin lounge for early risers, and Selena helped herself, warming her hands around the steaming cup.

A figure was standing on the outer deck at the bow, wearing a suede jacket and a scarf tied around her head. It took Selena a few minutes to recognize it was Julia. With her cup in her hand, she walked back on deck to join the woman.

"Good morning, Julia."

The woman turned, smiling automatically yet with a touch of absentness. "Good morning, Selena. You're up early."

"I couldn't sleep."

There was silence as Julia gazed intently ahead. The *Delta Queen* glided under a railroad bridge. Around the bend, a highway bridge stretched high across the river. There was a suggestion of activity concentrated behind the river's treed banks. It was this that held Julia's attention.

As if sensing Selena's curious eyes on her, Julia explained, "That's Vicksburg ahead."

Selena hesitated an instant before saying, "You do know we aren't stopping, don't you?"

"Yes." It was a quiet word, but it spoke volumes about Julia's disappointment.

Again there was silence as the boat moved steadily nearer. The wind gusted, tearing through Selena's uncovered hair. The sun was yellow, the streaks of dawn gone from the sky.

"I sent Leslie a wire telling him we wouldn't be stopping here," Julia said softly, "I hope he received it,"

"I'm sure he did," Selena consoled.

Selena waited with Julia while she maintained her silent vigil on the bow until the *Delta Queen* followed the channel markers past the mouth of the Yazoo River. Only then did the older woman suggest that they go inside. Vicksburg was behind them and Memphis was ahead.

Later that afternoon, Selena came up from the Orleans Room after watching a navigation film. Afternoon tea was being served in the aft cabin lounge. Wanting some fresh air, she decided to walk along the outer cabin deck to get to the aft section instead of using the wide passageway through the center of the deck.

At a leisurely pace, she began walking beside the railing to the stern. A cabin window was open, releasing familiar voices from within. Selena realized she was approaching Julia's stateroom. When she heard her name on Chance's lips, she stopped.

She didn't hear what Chance had said about her, but she heard Julia reply. "How can you say that? Selena is such a wonderful girl. You should know that by now from spending time with her on this cruise."

Since her insistence last night that Chance leave her alone, he had been remarkably absent all day. Selena didn't know how long it would last, but she realized that even Julia had noticed how much time he had been spending in her company.

There was a moment of pregnant silence from the cabin. Selena was afraid that Chance was going to tell Julia the sordid circumstances of their first meeting.

Instead he offered an impatient, "You're entirely too trusting, Julia. Sooner of later—"

"You think she's going to hurt me, don't you?" came Julia's gentle response. "In one way or another, I can practically guarantee it," he retorted.

A fellow passenger was walking toward Selena and she realized she didn't dare tarry any longer outside Julia's window or she would risk being discovered eavesdropping. She moved on, knowing Chance was still wrong about her. And she certainly would never do anything that would hurt Julia.

Two mornings later the *Delta Queen* steamed into Memphis. The sky was slate gray with a steady drizzle of rain coming from its clouds.

Selena stood beside Julia on the outer cabin deck beneath the overhang of the deck above them as the boat maneuvered to tie up. Despite the miserable weather, spectators were on the river front to watch the boat's arrival.

It was these faces that Julia searched so anxiously. When the lines were tied and the gangplank secure on the cobble-stoned ramp, she turned to Selena.

"Leslie isn't there," she announced, pain obvious in her expression.

"It's a little before nine and we weren't scheduled to arrive until nine, so maybe he doesn't know the boat is in yet," Selena suggested. "He still might come."

"I'll bet he didn't get the message to come to Memphis," Julia sighed.

As the minutes stretched into half an hour, Selena had to admit it was possible that Leslie had not received Julia's message. Silently she berated Chance for not being here to comfort his aunt.

"Listen," Selena said, refusing to give up, "why don't I go ashore and telephone the different hotels to see if I can find out where he's staying? Maybe he overslept."

"Oh, thank you, but I can't ask you to do that."

"You aren't asking me. I'm volunteering." She opened her purse and took out a piece of paper and pencil. "What's Leslie's full name?"

"Leslie Reid." Julia spelled it for her.

Selena slid the paper into her purse. "Is there any chance he might he staying with family or friends here in Memphis?"

"I don't think so," Julia replied, shaking her head uncertainly. "When Leslie and I were on the autumn cruise, we stopped in Memphis. He didn't mention knowing anyone here and I'm sure he would have."

"That just leaves the hotels and motels," Selena smiled, trying not to think about what a daunting list that would prove to be in a city the size of Memphis. "I'll be back as soon as I can. Wish me luck."

She was off, entering the forward cabin lounge and descending the stairs to the main deck and the gangplank. The light rain made the cobblestones slippery. It was tricky going until Selena reached the sidewalk.

The downtown shopping mall was only a few blocks from the dock. Every other building along the waterfront seemed to be occupied by cotton brokers or cotton warehouses. As she crossed the street, the clouds opened up, nearly drowning Selena in a downpour. No umbrella, bareheaded, wearing a cotton jacket that wasn't waterproofed, she was soon soaked to the skin before she could reach any kind of shelter.

Two hours later, with a pocketful of change consumed by the telephone booth in her fruitless search for Leslie's hotel, she made her way back through the driving rain, now being whipped by a cold north wind. Her feet slithered and slipped down the slanting cobblestones to the boat.

She was drenched by the rain, nearly frozen into an ice cube by the cold wind and disheartened by the long list of calls she had made in vain. At the back of her mind, she kept hoping that Leslie would be aboard the boat when she got there.

Someone was walking up the cobblestones directly toward her. At the moment her footing was fairly solid. She didn't care who it was, she wasn't going to give ground. He could just go around her.

The person kept coming directly toward her, not altering his path an inch. She didn't dare take her eyes off the uneven ground for fear of slipping and landing ignominiously on her backside.

"I thought country girls like you were supposed to have enough sense to come in out of the rain," Chance declared in an exasperated and mocking tone.

Selena stopped at the sound of his voice, glaring at him through the strands of the hair plastered across her eyes. "That's what I'm trying to do, if you'd get out of my way." Her teeth chattered uncontrollably when she spoke.

His arm circled her waist, providing solid support as he half lifted and half carried her to the more secure footing of the gangplank. He didn't slow the pace until they were under the shelter of the main deck.

"Where were you during the first half of that descent?" Selena muttered between shivers.

"You look like a drowned rat," Chance observed.

"Thanks a lot!" She was shaking all over, frozen to the bone.

The arm around her waist pushed her to the staircase. "What was so urgent that you had to go out in the middle of a downpour?" he demanded.

"I had to make some telephone calls," she answered, gritting her teeth to keep them from clattering together. "To see if I could find where Leslie was staying. Did he show up here at the boat?"

"Of all the harebrained, wild-goose chases—" Abruptly he cut off his exclamation and snapped, "No, he didn't."

"Poor Julia," Selena sighed. "She'll be heartbroken. You should be with her."

"I'm going to talk to her, all right." There was an ominous note in his voice. "But first you're going up to your cabin and get out of these wet clothes."

74

"That is where I was going," she retorted with as much strength as her shivering voice could muster. "Or did, you think I was going to wear them until they dried?"

"I wouldn't put it past you," Chance muttered, forcibly ushering her through the forward cabin lounge, unmindful of the gawking passengers. "Any fool that would go out in a downpour without a raincoat or an umbrella—" he pushed open the door to the outer deck and shoved Selena through "—might not have enough brains to change into dry clothes."

"It was only drizzling when I left," she defended. "And I'm not made of sugar. I don't melt."

He gave her a cutting look and demanded, "Where's your room key?"

"In my bag."

Before Selena could open it, he was taking the bag from her shaking hands and pushing her up the stairs to the texas deck. Her reactions weren't as quick as they normally were.

Before she could stop her impetus forward and protest at his taking of her purse, Chance had found the key and was handing back her purse. He hustled her the rest of the way up the stairs to her cabin door, opening it and pushing her inside.

Now that she was out of the wind and the rain she was shivering even worse. She stopped short when she realized that Chance had followed her into the cabin.

"Get out of here," she shuddered impatiently. "I want to change my clothes."

He gave her a raking glance that told her what a sorry sight she was. It didn't do much for her self-confidence. "I brought you here to change your clothes, so get undressed."

Her mouth opened to order him out, but he was already brushing past her into the bathroom. He emerged a second later with a bath towel in his hand.

"Are you going to undress yourself or am I going to do it for you?" he challenged.

The hard set of his jaw warned her that there was no use arguing. She would simply be wasting her time and expending energy in a useless effort. Shuddering from the bone-chilling wetness of her clothes, she gritted her teeth and lifted her numbed fingers to her blouse buttons. If they had been all thumbs, they couldn't have been more awkward.

"You could at least turn around," she snapped, blaming his intent gaze for her fumbling efforts.

Chance ignored her request. "The clothes will be dry before you ever get them off." He pushed her hands away and began unbuttoning the blouse.

"I can do it myself," Selena protested almost tearfully, angered and miserable to the point where she wanted to cry.

75

"There is a time for modesty, Red—" he stripped the blouse from her shoulders and gave it a toss into the bathroom "—and this isn't it."

He shoved her, down to sit on the bed while he knelt to remove the saturated leather shoes from her feet. They followed her blouse into the bathroom, along with her socks. Impersonally, Chance reached up and unsnapped her pants. Grabbing the sodden material of the pants legs, he pulled those off, too. Then he rose and pivoted to pull down the covers of the other single bed.

"Wrap the towel around your head and get into bed, little miss prim and proper," he ordered. "While you're hiding under the covers, you can take your underclothes off."

He waited until Selena had done as she was told. When the underclothes were lying in a wet heap beside the floor, he turned and left the cabin. Continuing to shiver, Selena closed her eyes and snuggled deeper under the covers, certain she would never be warm again. But at least Chance was gone.

After fifteen minutes, she began to warm through and feel like a human being again. There was a warning rattle of metal, then the door opened and Chance walked through, carrying a tray.

"The door was locked!" she protested angrily.

"I took the key with me," he explained offhandedly, and slipped it into his pocket.

"Why don't you go away and leave me alone? You've had your laugh at my expense. Now go away!" Selena cried in frustration, in no position to enforce her demand. "I—"

"I've brought you some soup from the kitchen," Chance interrupted as if he hadn't heard a word she'd said.

"Leave it on the chest of drawers."

He sat down on the edge of the bed beside her, balancing the tray on his knees. As he removed the cover from the bowl, the mouth-watering smell of chicken soup filled the room. Picking up the soup spoon, he dipped out some broth and carried the spoon to her lips. Selena couldn't believe it. He was actually going to feed her.

"Come on, eat up," Chance ordered calmly, forcing the metal spoon between her lips.

She swallowed it, the liquid warming her throat as it went down. When he put the spoon in the bowl again, Selena couldn't help smiling.

"You look ridiculous," she said. He flicked an impassive glance in her direction and started to bring the spoon to her mouth. "Any minute I expect to hear you say, open the hangar, here comes the airplane, just as if you were feeding a child."

"Are you going to eat or talk?" he questioned.

76

"I'm going to eat." Selena pushed herself into more of a sitting position, taking her arms from beneath the covers while keeping the blankets tucked securely across her front. "But I'm going to feed myself."

With a shrug of acceptance, Chance shifted the tray so that it was on her lap and slid another pillow behind her head to prop her up.

"Have you seen Julia to tell her I couldn't find Leslie registered at any of the hotels?" Selena asked between spoonfuls.

"Not yet," he answered with a grim look.

"I feel so sorry for her," she sighed.

"My aunt doesn't need your pity."

"Well, she certainly doesn't get any from you!" she retorted, stung by his roughness. "You couldn't care less if Leslie ever shows up and you know it."

Chance eyed her narrowly. "There's a great deal that you don't know about my aunt and me and my family. I suggest that you aren't in any position to condemn my behavior since you aren't in possession of all the facts."

"Then tell me the facts," she challenged.

"I don't discuss personal family matters with strangers. And you, Red…despite all the intimate moments we've shared or almost shared—" there was a mocking glint in his steady look "—you're a stranger."

Selena's hunger for the soup ended with his words. She set the spoon on the tray and handed it to him. "I don't want any more," she said stiffly. Grudgingly she added, "Thank you for bringing it."

"It was the least I could do," he said, accepting thanks indifferently, "since it was at my aunt's instigation that you ended up half-drowned."

After Chance had left with the tray, Selena pulled the covers around her neck and slid down into a horizontal position. All his concern had been prompted by a sense of duty and responsibility. Nothing more.

She felt let down somehow, cheated out of a feeling that could have been exceedingly pleasant. She closed her eyes, trying to shut out the sensation. It wasn't long before she was asleep.

A hand touched her shoulder and she rolled over in alarm. She had difficulty focusing her vision, which was fuzzy from sleep. Chance was sitting on the bed, watching her with those intent black eyes.

"How do you feel?" He pressed his palm across her forehead, then turned it to let the back of his hand rest against her cheek.

"I'm fine." Her insistent voice was thick and husky from the sleep. He took his hand away in apparent satisfaction, assured that she wasn't running a fever.

"What are you doing here again?"

"I wanted to see how you were and whether you were going down to dinner tonight," he explained with a faintly amused twist of his mouth. "It's six o'clock."

77

"It can't be!" she frowned in protest.

"I'm sorry. Maybe it can't be, but it is," Chance shrugged. "So what's the decision? Are you coming down or do you want something sent up?"

"I'm coming down," Selena answered.

"Good. I'll wait for you outside." He straightened from the bed.

As he walked to the door, she said, "And leave my key on the chest of drawers."

There was a jangle of metal as the key was deposited on the wooden top before Chance walked out of the door. She heard the click of the lock and slipped out of bed to dress hurriedly.

Most of the passengers were already in the dining room when Selena and Chance arrived at the staircase leading to the Orleans Room. Another couple approached the stairs at the same time. Both men gave way to permit the women to go first.

"How are you feeling?" the woman inquired of Selena.

"Fine," she blinked in surprise.

"That was quite a drenching you got today. It's a miracle you didn't catch your death of cold."

"I never get sick," Selena replied.

"A person can never be too careful at this time of year. I've had more colds in spring than any other time of year," the woman remarked. "It was probably a good thing that you stayed in your cabin and rested and kept warm this afternoon."

"Yes." *Good heavens,* Selena thought, *how much more does this woman know about me?*

At the bottom of the stairs, the woman paused and smiled. "It must have made you feel good the way Chance looked after you, bringing you hot soup and all. I couldn't think of anyone nicer to take care of me than him—unless of course it was my husband," she laughed.

Selena echoed it weakly before the couple separated from them to go to their own table. If every person in the dining room had turned to look at her with Chance, she couldn't have felt more self-conscious.

As Chance escorted her to their table where Julia waited, Selena asked in a low, accusing tone, "Does everyone on board know about my rain-soaked morning?"

"Probably," he conceded, amusement glinting in his downward glance at her rigidly set expression of composure.

"Did you have to tell them?" she muttered in an aside before greeting the woman at the table. "Hello, Julia."

"How are you feeling, Selena?" came the question of concern.

"Fine," she said, and wondered how many times she was going to have to repeat the answer before the evening was over.

78

She sat down in the chair Chance held out for her. As he helped her slide it closer to the table, he bent low to murmur a taunt near her ear. "Would you have preferred that I didn't explain what I was doing in your cabin in the middle of the day?" Her color rose briefly, giving him the answer that didn't need to be put into words.

Straightening, he took the chair opposite Selena while she attempted to concentrate her attention on Julia. "I'm sorry I—" She was about to apologize and offer her sympathy for not being able to find any trace of Leslie.

Julia broke in with a radiant smile, "Did Chance tell you the news? I've heard from Leslie!"

"No, he didn't." She flashed him a reproving glance, not understanding why he had omitted that when he knew how concerned she was for Julia. "That's wonderful!"

"Yes, it is." The older woman was brimming with happiness.

"Did you explain why he wasn't in Memphis to meet you?" Selena asked.

"Yes. There was some mix-up and he didn't receive my message in time to get to Memphis before the boat left. He's driving to Louisville now," Julia told her.

Again Selena couldn't help noticing the profound silence surrounding Chance, just as it had other times when the subject of discussion was Leslie. She also noticed the way he deftly changed the subject at the first opportunity, drawing Selena's attention to the menu choices so that the waiter might take their order.

When the main course was served, Julia asked, "Are you wearing a costume to the Mardi Gras party tomorrow night, Selena?"

"Is it tomorrow night? I hadn't realized," she replied. "I had thought about dressing up in costume when I heard about it, but…" She let the sentence trail off. Tomorrow night didn't give her much time to come up with anything. She cast a curious look at Chance. "Are you going to wear a costume?"

"I might. I hadn't thought about it."

"You could always come as a riverboat gambler," Selena suggested, half seriously, "with a string tie and brocade vest."

"That's an idea," Chance agreed smoothly. "And you could be a saloon girl."

"Except that I don't have the costume for that," she corrected, not liking his needling innuendo.

"Of course, you don't have to be in the costume to attend the party," Julia inserted. "The majority of the passengers probably won't, but it does make it so much more fun when you participate in the spirit of the event."

Selena started to make a comment, but Chance's low voice came first. "Your orange dress would work well as a costume."

She was about to remind him that she didn't have it anymore when she realized that he undoubtedly did. "Perhaps," she agreed curtly, expecting any second for Julia to ask how Chance knew about a dress that Selena hadn't worn while on the boat. "But there are other parts to the costume than just the dress."

"You'd need to wear your hair up, glue a black beauty spot on your cheek and wear a black ribbon around your neck," Chance listed. "I'm sure one of the boys in the band would lend you his garter."

"And I have a black boa you could borrow," Julia offered. "One of those silly feathery things. There's crêpe paper you could use to make an ornament for your hair. I think it's a terrific idea."

Selena had little room left for argument. "Okay, I'll go as a saloon girl—as long as you go as a riverboat gambler, Chance," she qualified.

"You have a deal, Red." His mouth twitched in amusement, his expression otherwise bland.

She had once said she wouldn't wear that dress again if she did get it back. And here she was, blackmailing herself into wearing it to a party—with Chance. She didn't understand how she had talked herself into it. But it had been easy. The words had come out before she had the sense to say she wasn't going to wear a costume,

Suppressing a sigh, she sliced a bite of stuffed pork chop. With her mouth full of food, surely she wouldn't have room for her foot.

8

Selena knew she wouldn't have missed the party the following night for anything. An extraordinary number of passengers came in costumes, parading down the stairwell to the Orleans Room. There was a highly imaginative assortment from sheeted ghosts to a Roman warrior, courtesy of the pots and pans from the kitchen. The range went from the ridiculous to the sublime.

After the parade of costumes and entertainment by the crew and passengers alike came the late-night snacks followed by dance music from the band. Selena was too caught up in the party spirit to leave when the music began, nor did Chance suggest they should.

Instead he turned to her and asked, rather mockingly, "Is it permitted for a minister's daughter to dance?"

Selena was simply in too good a mood to take offense. "It is for this minister's daughter," she smiled, and let him lead her onto the floor.

As he turned her into his arms, she felt again his manly strength, the power contained, the firm arm around her waist. She remembered the other times Chance had held her in his arms to kiss her, make love to her, and immediately shied away from those memories.

Chance bent his head slightly to better see her face. "I never thought I'd see you again in that red dress," he smiled wryly.

"I never thought I'd wear it again," Selena returned in a matching tone.

He was dangerously charming tonight, flirting with her in his mocking way. The admiring light in those lazy black eyes made her feel very special. She would have been neither human nor female if she had tried to deny that she liked it.

With each dance, it became easier to match his steps, to let her body sway with his in tempo with the music. Her senses came alive in his embrace. Whatever resistance she might have had melted under the warmth of his body heat and the intimate pressure of his thighs brushing against hers. With each breath, she caught the scent of the lotion on his smooth cheeks, a heady mixture of spice and musk. And the steady rhythm of his heartbeat was hypnotic.

It was with regret that Selena left his arms when the last song ended. She shifted the feathery boa higher up around her shoulders as the hand at the small of her back guided her from the floor to the stairs.

"Shall we take the long way to our cabins?" Chance suggested.

Selena nodded an affirmative answer, trying to steady the leap of her heart at his suggestion.

At an unhurried pace, they wandered onto the outer cabin deck to slowly make their way around the bow to the texas stairs. A half moon was beaming a silvery light from the midnight sky. The air was briskly cool, invigorating to senses already sharply aware of everything around them.

Climbing the stairs, they made a circuitous route around the texas deck. Neither spoke, not wanting to break the spell that was somehow making the evening seem so special.

As they rounded the stern where the paddle wheel splashed rhythmically in its circle, a sudden breeze whipped the trailing end of the black boa, sending it across Selena's face before the gust of wind faded. The fluff tickled her nose and she sneezed.

"Are you catching cold?" Chance stopped, studying her intently.

Selena shook her head. "No. It was just these feathers."

"It is chilly, though, and you should have something on your arms." He took his hand away from her to slip off his jacket, mocking himself as he said, "Therefore I will do the gentlemanly thing and offer you my coat."

"I'm all right, really," Selena protested.

But he was already swinging his jacket behind her to drape it over her shoulders. As he drew the lapels together in front of her, his enigmatic dark eyes focused on her lips. She held her breath, her heart beating a mile a minute. His fingers tightened on the material, pulling her toward him. And she realized it was what she had been waiting for all evening.

His head blacked out the half moon as he moved toward hers. His mouth was hungry in its possession, its appetite insatiable, taking, devouring and always demanding more. His hard length pushed her into the shadows of the overhang, pinning her against the wooden frame of the boat.

There was no pressure, no force to make her submit. No, the insidious seduction was taking place within her, making her hands weak and trembling as they spread across the solid muscles of his shoulders.

When he lifted his head, it was to bury his cheek in the flaming silk of her hair. "Selena." His demanding voice was rough, his breathing equally so. "If I ever find out you aren't a minister's daughter, I'll wring your neck!"

She laughed softly, but it hurt, as did the unsatisfied ache she felt inside. "I never felt less like a minister's daughter in my life," she answered.

Chance nipped at her earlobe. "I never felt more like saying to hell with propriety."

She shuddered against him, knowing how much she echoed his sentiments, and he gathered her close, pressing her face into his chest, his hands running caressingly over her spine.

"Cold?"

"I wish I were," Selena murmured, and felt him smile against her hair.

"Now you know at least a little of the way I feel," he said, and sighed heavily. "I'm not used to playing these games, of being satisfied with kisses. In the past, I've always taken what I wanted with few exceptions. Then you come along with your damned red hair and green eyes—and the menacing specter of your father, the reverend. And I get the awful feeling I'm being reformed."

Selena drew her head away from his chest to look up at him. "Chance, I—"

He kissed her hard to silence the response, leaving her breathless when he was through. "Let's get to your cabin before my better judgment gets pushed aside," he said roughly.

But it was a gentle arm that encircled her shoulders and guided Selena to her cabin. Chance took the key from her hand and unlocked the door, but she didn't immediately enter. Flirting with danger, she looked up at him, her eyes still luminous with the emotions he had aroused.

"Chance, I—" she tried again to speak.

His mouth tightened as he pressed his hand across her lips. "Just say good night, Red," he ordered.

"Good night," Selena complied, and returned his jacket before slipping quietly inside the door.

In the room, she listened to him walk to the railing. She partly understood his reluctance to talk about what was happening between them. She was confused, too. At times, she disliked him intensely, distrusted him. She didn't know what her, true feelings were. Possibly he didn't, either.

With a sigh, she began undressing. As she hung the red dress up on a hanger, she remembered that Chance still hadn't returned the matching shawl. She would have to ask him about it tomorrow.

Although he was outside, she knew he was right that the evening was at an end for them tonight. There were a few things they had to think about before they met each other in the morning.

The next morning Selena awakened to discover the boat was tied up at Paducah, Kentucky, to take on fresh water for the boilers. In the night the Mississippi River had been left and the *Delta Queen* had entered the Ohio River.

When she went down to breakfast, Julia was at their table, but not Chance. There were indications at his place setting that he'd been there and gone.

"Good morning, Selena. Did you and Chance dance all night?" Julia had retired the past evening when the dancing had started.

"We tried," she admitted, taking her chair. Her gaze slid to the empty chair opposite hers. "He must have been up early this morning."

"Yes. He was leaving as I came down," Julia told her. "He seemed restless, as if he had something on his mind. He said he was going to walk into town."

Regret swept through Selena. She would have gladly gone with him if he had asked. Subdued, she ordered her breakfast, discovering that she wasn't nearly as hungry as she had thought.

She was in the forward cabin lounge when Chance returned, within minutes of the boat's departure. A newspaper was tucked under his arm as he climbed the stairs from the main deck. He smiled and wished her good morning, then walked to the coffee urn to pour himself a cup before settling in one of the sofas to read the paper.

Expecting something more demonstrative, Selena managed to hide her disappointment and began chatting with some of the other passengers in the lounge. When the boat was well under way, she wandered outside.

After a week of viewing the levee-lined banks of the Mississippi and the flatlands stretching beyond them, the scenery along the Ohio River provided a startling contrast. Massive hills came right up to the water's edge on one side, their heavily treed slopes permitting occasional glimpses of rock faces.

The other side of the river was valley farmland with more hills in the distance. Selena noticed these features alternated. One time the hills would be on the right and the valley on the left. Around the bend, the positions would be reversed.

The buildings along the river ranged from farm homes to ramshackle huts to beautiful country homes. The wind turned brisk and blustery, forcing Selena to the lee side of the boat, where she watched the changing scenery alone.

Not until the afternoon did Chance seek her out. He was friendly and charming, but something was missing. She had the distinct impression that he had withdrawn behind that bronze mask his features could set to conceal his true feelings from the outside world.

The previous night with all its hinted-at changes might never have happened. Selena wondered if it had or whether she had only imagined the difference in Chance's attitude last night.

The next afternoon there was kite flying off the stern of the sun deck. Selena had assembled her kite in the aft cabin lounge and was carrying it up to the sun deck when she met Chance.

"Well, if it isn't Mrs. Benjamin Franklin!" he mocked, his eyes crinkling at the corners.

"Why don't you go fly a kite?" she suggested laughingly.

"I certainly hope you don't intend to fly that one," Chance commented, eyeing her kite skeptically.

"Why not?" She looked at it, finding nothing wrong.

"Because it won't fly. Didn't you follow the instructions when you put it together?"

"I couldn't understand the directions." Selena gave a helpless little shrug. "But I thought it looked like a kite when I was through."

"Here." He reached for the kite. "The string is tied wrong, I'll fix it for you."

Obligingly Selena handed him the kite and its ball of twine. With quick, sure movements, he cut away her work and rethreaded the string properly through the kite before he gave it back to her.

"Have you ever flown a kite before?" he asked.

"No," she admitted with a dimpling smile.

"Then may I come along to view the launching? It's bound to be something to see." The grooves around his mouth were deepening in an effort to hold back a smile. It didn't matter because his eyes were laughing at her.

"Very well," Selena agreed readily. "But don't make fun of me."

"Would I do something like that?" His voice was heavy with mock innocence. "Yes."

There were quite a few fellow kite-flying passengers on the sun deck when they reached it, but only two kites were actually in the air. The rest were still trying.

After Selena made four unsuccessful attempts to get her kite airborn, Chance stepped forward to offer some advice. Under his direction she succeeded on the next attempt.

"Give it a little more string." Chance stood close behind her, and her shoulder brushed against his chest as she obeyed his instructions.

"More string."

"It's flying! It's actually flying!" she breathed, her eyes sparkling. The words were barely out when the kite began looping crazily like a wild thing trying to free itself from tether. "What's wrong?" she asked, frantically feeding out more line.

"I think it's caught in the down drafts created by the paddle-wheel's rotation," Chance answered, watching the erratic behavior of the kite. At that moment it swooped, diving for the red paddle wheel. "Look out! You're going to lose it."

Jointly they attempted to reel the string in to rescue the kite from the churning paddles. For a few seconds, it looked as if they were going to save it. Then it was gone.

"That red monster ate my kite!" Selena declared with a mock sigh.

"We'll see how everybody else fares," Chance smiled.

No longer participating in the flying, they stood to one side and watched the others. The "red monster" had a voracious appetite. It gobbled up more of the kites until there were only six left, soaring high out of reach of the paddle wheel. It became a contest to see which kite could fly the highest, and more balls of string were added to each kite.

A practical joker in the spectators called out, "Bring them in. There's a bridge just around the bend!"

There was a moment of panic until the kite flyers realized their legs were being pulled. There were numerous threats to throw the joker overboard, but all six kites remained on the boat.

Gradually the crowd of spectators thinned, and Chance and Selena wandered to an empty section of the port railing. Chance rested his elbows on the teak wood and leaned forward, clasping his hands in front of him. The sun was hot and the breeze was cool, a perfect combination. Selena laid her hands on the railing and lifted her face to the wind and sun.

With no advance warning of his topic, Chance said, "I had my secretary call the charity you said you sent the money to in New Orleans."

His announcement caught Selena completely off guard. Stunned, she could only look at him, unable to make any response. He glanced over his shoulder, noting her reaction.

"The charity admitted that they had received that amount of cash from an anonymous donor," he finished.

Finally she found her voice. "Are you convinced now that I've been telling you the truth?"

"Yes." He straightened from the railing and turned to her, his gaze steady as it met hers. "I owe you an apology, Selena, for my behavior in New Orleans and aboard this boat."

Her smile was a mixture of chagrin and ruefulness. "It wasn't entirely your fault that you got the wrong impression about me," she felt bound to admit.

"Do you forgive me?" '

"Of course."

"You're very generous," Chance remarked dryly, turning away to study the valley farmland the boat was approaching. "If the situation was reversed, I don't know if I would be that ready to forgive." She was about to make a response when he distracted her attention. "Look!"

She followed the direction of his pointing finger and saw a small boy racing across a plowed field toward the river, running and stumbling over the clods of dirt. He wanted to reach the bank before the Delta Queen went by. Selena held her breath, afraid he wouldn't make it and knowing he was running his heart out.

"He's going to make it," Chance announced.

"Do you think so?" Selena doubted.

"This isn't exactly a speedboat," he chided.

Just as the bow of the steamboat glided past a grassy area on the bank, the boy reached the same spot. Winded, a sandy mop of hair tousled by his race, he began waving wildly, a broad grin slitting his freckled face. Selena waved back with equal enthusiasm along with Chance.

When they had glided past and the red paddle wheel was churning its goodbye, Selena continued to watch the figure on the bank growing steadily smaller.

"How exciting it must be for a small boy to see a boat like the Delta Queen steaming up the river," she commented. "How exciting for anyone. I guess children can just better express it."

"True," Chance agreed absently, and moved away from the railing, unexpectedly adding, "I'll see you at dinner."

After his apology, she had thought that his air of remoteness would leave. But there was a part of him that was still reserved and aloof. He was holding back and she didn't know why.

On Wednesday, the Delta Queen arrived in Louisville, Kentucky. For the third time, Selena stood on deck with Julia as the boat docked, unable to believe that Leslie would fail to appear again. Yet there was no one waiting on the waterfront except an obliging deckhand from the Belle of Louisville to help them tie up.

Cars and trucks whizzed by on the elevated interstate highway system passing above the wharf, some honking at the Delta Queen as she docked. The crew members not involved in the tying up were busy decking out the boat in all her finery. Pennants streamed from her landing boom and bunting was draped on her railings, all in festive preparation for the great steamboat race later in the day.

Neither woman felt festive as they turned away from the railing. Selena was confused and concerned. The same expression was mirrored in Julia's face along with aching disappointment.

"What do you suppose happened this time?" Selena asked.

"I don't know," Julia shook her head bewilderedly. "Leslie said he was driving straight here. He should have arrived at least by Monday. I can't think why he's not here."

"Would you like me to go ashore and make some telephone calls?"

"Oh, no, I can't let you do that—not after the last time," Julia refused hurriedly. "Chance would never forgive me."

"Chance doesn't have any say in what I do," Selena answered with a trace of irritation.

"Perhaps not." But Julia didn't exactly concede the point. "But I think I should make the calls. Would you stay on the boat in case Leslie comes while I'm gone?"

"Yes—"

"He's a tall, rather strongly built man, plain-looking, with a mustache, and he always wears a hat." A smile touched the older woman's mouth as she described him.

"I'll watch for him," Selena promised.

Twenty minutes after Julia had left, Chance came by, looking vitally masculine in a blue blazer and gray slacks. He gave Selena one of those disarming smiles that reached his eyes. She felt her heart flutter at the sight of him, so handsome and so male.

"Shall we do some sight-seeing in Louisville?" he suggested. "Go out to Churchill Downs and see if we can pick the Derby winner on Saturday?"

"I'm sorry." She hated to refuse, wanting very much to accept his invitation. "I promised Julia I'd wait here in case Leslie arrived while she was gone."

His mouth immediately thinned, his features chilling into hard lines. "Leslie isn't—" he began impatiently, then abruptly cut off the rest of the sentence.

But Selena had heard enough to take a wild guess that it would have been, "Leslie isn't coming." Her look became wary and accusing.

"Leslie isn't coming?" She demanded that he finish it. "What do you know about this?"

The bland mask slipped into place. "I don't know anything about it," he returned smoothly.

"I was simply going to say that Leslie isn't your affair."

"I don't see it that way." Her reply was stiff; she still did not quite believe his explanation.

He seemed to shrug although Selena detected no movement. Perhaps it was his attitude of indifference that gave her that impression.

He moved away, adding coolly, "I'll see you later," over his shoulder.

It was the middle of the afternoon before Julia returned, disheartened by her fruitless efforts to find or contact Leslie and upset by his unexplained

88

absence. The state of her nerves wasn't improved by the influx of photographers and cameramen and various other members of the news media aboard to cover the race, or the hundred or so extra passengers who were coming on the *Delta Queen* just for the race.

"Why don't you lie down in your room for a while?" Selena suggested. "I'll tell the chief purser and the porters where you are. If a message comes from Leslie, then they'll know exactly where to find you."

"Yes, perhaps you're right," Julia agreed, her hands twisting in agitation. "I'll do that."

Selena spent some time in Julia's room, trying to calm her down and offer some words of reassurance, however meager. When she returned to the outer deck, the railing was crowded with passengers, the regular list and the new intruders.

The deep, rasping whistle of the *Delta Queen* blasted its long-and-two-shorts signal that it was leaving port. The *Belle of Louisville* was already in midstream along with the starter's boat. A crowd of spectators stood behind the barricades on the dock. The great steamboat race was about to get under way. Reversing into the channel, the *Delta Queen* moved upstream to draw level with the *Belle.*

"The railroad bridge overhead is the starting line." Chance was at her elbow, holding a mint julep in each hand.

"Thank you." As Selena took one of them, the paddle wheels on each boat stopped turning and they floated toward the bridge.

When the bows of the boats reached the imaginary line, the cannon on the starter's boat went off. Smoke billowed from the stacks and, the paddle wheels began rotating again, churning up the water.

Yet nothing seemed to be happening. They were inching forward at a snail's pace, no explosive acceleration, no leap forward. The passengers on each boat were yelling. "Go! Go! Go!" Selena couldn't help laughing at the exceedingly slow start, so very different from the beginning of any other race.

"I told you before, this isn't a speedboat," Chance murmured dryly. "The *Belle* is shorter and lighter. She'll get up steam and power first and move into the lead. It takes the *Delta Queen* a little longer to get going. Then we'll catch up—I hope."

As he predicted, the *Belle of Louisville* took the early lead with the *Delta Queen* slowly closing the gap. Selena sipped at the sweet drink in her hand. The race was a very novel experience.

"How long is it?" she asked.

"Twelve miles. We go up to Six Mile Island and turn around," he explained. "The starting line is the finishing line, too. The race takes about two hours."

Both sides of the bank as far as Selena could see were lined with people, sometimes four and five rows deep, family groups picnicking while they

89

watched the two old-time riverboats churning up the Ohio. The helicopters carrying more members of the news media followed the race's course, swooping low, sometimes hovering above the two boats.

A roar went through the passengers on the *Delta Queen* as they realized she was pulling ahead. The crowds on the bank saved their cheers to encourage the hometown favorite, the *Belle of Louisville.*

They had not reached the halfway point when Chance suggested, "They have a buffet set up in the Orleans Room. Shall we eat before the rest of the passengers decide to crowd down there?"

Selena agreed readily, knowing they would have plenty of time to eat and be back on deck for the finish of this unique race. Only a few other people had the same idea as Chance, so the room was fairly empty. They helped themselves to the buffet and sat down at their regular table. They were halfway through the meal when the *Delta Queen* was jolted.

"What was that?" Selena looked up in alarm.

"A towboat," Chance explained as they were jolted again. "We've reached Six Mile Island and are turning around. There are two towboats waiting, one for us and one for the *Belle*, to help us make a sharp, clean turnaround."

With the turn complete, the *Delta Queen* headed downstream, tooting her hoarse whistle twice. For a moment, Selena didn't understand the implication of the signal. Then it struck her. The pilot was signaling to the *Belle* that they would be passing on the starboard side.

The *Belle of Louisville* was still coming upstream, not having reached the turnaround point, and they were heading down, well in the lead. Suddenly the whistles carried the sweet ring of victory.

"We're going to win, aren't we?" she smiled at Chance.

"Barring a catastrophe," he agreed.

Her gaze slid to the empty chair Julia usually occupied, and some of the delight left her as she remembered that the older woman was in her room, heartsick and worried by Leslie's absence.

"I wonder why Leslie wasn't here to meet Julia," she mused aloud.

"I don't know," was the sharply clipped response from Chance.

Her temper flared at his curt words. "What you mean is that you don't care!"

"I don't know exactly what I mean." This time he spoke calmly and concisely. "But I don't want to get into a discussion about it now."

"You never want to discuss it." She was suddenly very close to tears.

"Selena—" His voice was husky, stroking her like thick, rough velvet.

"You can save your charm. It isn't going to make me forget how you're treating Julia, trying to deprive her of what future happiness she might find with Leslie."

90

There was more she wanted to say, but there was a painful lump in her throat. Jerkily she pushed away from the table and walked stiffly from the room, ignoring his low command to come back.

It was easy to lose herself in the crowd on deck. If Chance searched for her in the milling throng, he didn't find her. As the *Delta Queen* crossed the finish line first, Selena cheered along with the rest, but hers rang hollow-amidst the whistles of victory. She felt chilled and empty inside. Her heart was elsewhere.

9

The next day Selena stood on deck alone and watched the Delta Queen pulling away from Madison, Indiana, after their morning's stop, a town renowned for its classic examples of fine architecture. Everything and everyone on the riverboat seemed quieter, the excitement of yesterday's race over and the realization that tomorrow morning they would be in Cincinnati, journey's end.

With a sigh, she turned from the railing and walked into the forward lounge. Just as she entered, she saw Julia walking toward the passageway leading to her stateroom. There was no spring to her step and no happiness in her expression. A surge of compassion swept through Selena at the agony of uncertainty and confusion the older woman was going through.

"My, you look glum, Miss Merrick," a voice commented. "I hope your cruise with us has been more enjoyable than your expression indicates!"

Selena turned to find Doug Spender, the chief purser, standing beside her. She forced a smile, "I've enjoyed the cruise very much. I was thinking about Julia...Miss Barkley—" she glanced in the direction the older woman had taken "—and wishing there was something I could do. I feel so sorry for her."

"Yes, I know what you mean," he agreed. "All of us in the crew, especially the ones that have been with the *Delta Queen* for several years, are very fond of Miss Julia. It seems a shame that she keeps putting herself through this year after year."

Selena found his comment curious and looked at him with a frown. "I beg your pardon?"

"Don't you know?" An eyebrow arched in faint surprise.

"Know what?" she questioned.

"Leslie has been dead for fifteen years. He was killed in a car crash on his way to Louisville to meet Miss Julia," the chief purser explained.

"No!" Selena paled. "No, I didn't know that."

"It's true. Tragic but true," he concluded.

"Mr. Spender!" One of the other passengers approached to claim the chief purser's attention.

Shaken by the information, Selena left the room in a daze, unaware of where she was going until the briskness of fresh air touched her skin. She was on the outer deck. With a trembling hand, she groped for the support of the railing.

She couldn't take it all in. Leslie was dead. He had been for fifteen years. And Julia, dear sweet Julia, was going through the whole sequence of events again, probably just as it had happened fifteen years ago. A sob bubbled in her throat, and she swallowed it back. Poor Julia, she thought.

"Selena, are you all right?" Chance was beside her, studying her waxen complexion with concern.

She looked at him, a fine mist of tears blurring her vision. "I've just found out…about Leslie," she explained tightly. "He's dead."

"Ah, yes." His features were suddenly grim and there was a sardonic inflection in his voice. "Julia must have got the message about the accident now."

His response struck a raw nerve. "You're a cruel, heartless man. You don't have any compassion at all!" Selena flared bitterly. "The happiest day in my life is going to be the day I get off this boat and see you for the last time! You're disgusting! Totally disgusting!"

With the last spitting word, she swept away from him to reenter the lounge. Inside the door, she hesitated for only a second before making her way to Julia's stateroom. It didn't matter that Leslie had been dead for so long. Julia still needed some comforting, and it was certain that Chance wouldn't provide it. Besides, Selena wanted to understand why Julia was doing this.

She knocked twice on the door, lightly, and heard Julia's muffled voice bid her enter. As Selena walked in, she saw the older woman tucking the message card back in its small envelope, the one that had accompanied the bouquet of roses delivered the first day of the cruise, the one that read "I love you. May I always and forever be—your Leslie." Selena felt the grip of poignancy in her throat.

"Selena, my dear, come in and sit down," Julia welcomed her graciously. "I was just—" she fingered the small envelope in her hand and smiled wistfully "—rereading the note Leslie sent me with the roses."

Selena took a seat on the bed near Julia. "I don't know how to say this exactly," she began hesitantly. "But I just found out that Leslie is dead."

Julia frowned, "No, that isn't until tomorrow." Then she lifted a hand to her lips, discovery of Selena's meaning dawning in her eyes. "Oh, someone has told you that he's been dead for some time. You must think I'm crazy for pretending he's still alive."

"No." Selena shook her head and would have added more.

But Julia interrupted with a wry smile. "If not crazy, then just a little bit eccentric."

"I just don't understand why you put yourself through this."

"But don't you see? It was the happiest time of my life," she explained. "Oh, it did end tragically for me when Leslie died, but before that I felt warm and alive and wonderful, knowing I was going to marry him."

Selena still didn't understand. It was revealed in the confusion of her green eyes. Julia took her hand gently, as one would take a child's, and patted it.

"I was an old maid threatening to turn into a starchy, stiff, older old maid, when I met Leslie sixteen years ago. My father always accused me of being too choosy. The truth was that I'd only received two proposals in my life, both from men I abhorred," she said with a mock shudder. "Then when Leslie came into my life, I began feeling like a real woman instead of an aging imitation. Maybe our marriage wouldn't have worked, as my family said, but I'll always be grateful to him for the way he changed me. When I lost him, I was afraid I'd turn into a bitter, starchy old maid, that I would shrivel up inside myself again. That's when I decided I had to keep taking this cruise."

"To renew the memories of how you felt." Selena was beginning to follow Julia's reasoning.

"It's a harmless game of make-believe I play in my mind. Until this trip, I've never involved anyone else in my pretending except a few members of the crew, whom I have know a long time."

"Yet this time you included me."

"Yes, I did," Julia admitted somewhat ruefully. "Perhaps I shouldn't have, but your reactions, your concern and interest made all the sensations so very real again. I hope you don't think badly of me. I truly meant no harm."

"I don't—I couldn't," Selena assured her, affection for the older woman gleaming in her eyes. "You've merely found an uncommon way to stay young

94

at heart. It was just a shock to learn that Leslie was dead, has been dead for some time. I was worried that—" She hesitated, uncertain of how to phrase it.

"That I was trying to bring Leslie back from the grave?" Julie inserted in the blank.

"Something like that, yes," Selena nodded.

"No, I only want to keep the gift of life that he gave me," Julia explained. "I loved him and I'm sorry I lost him. But it doesn't accomplish anything to forever mourn the loss of a loved one. You must learn to rejoice in the good things they left with you. That's all I'm trying to do."

"I understand." And she did.

"I was sure you would," Julia smiled. "After all, you know how it feels to be in love, how warm and deliciously alive it makes you feel inside."

"Me?" Selena echoed with a blank look.

"You've fallen in love with Chance, haven't you?" Julia tipped her head to the side on a questioning angle.

"I—" Selena started to deny it, then was jolted by the discovery that it was true. "I...have, yes."

"It's a grand feeling, isn't it?"

"It is," she agreed weakly, but the realization was too new for her to know exactly what her reaction to it was. An announcement came over the public-address system, but she was deaf to the sound, listening only to turnings of her own mind.

"They're serving tea in the aft lounge. Shall we go have some?" Julia suggested.

"What?" For a moment the question didn't register, then Selena shook her head, copper-colored hair moving briefly against her shoulders. "I have some packing to finish yet and I want to shower and change before the Captain's Dinner tonight." She rose from the bed and Julia stood, too.

"I think I will have a cup," she decided, then smiled. "In a way, it's something of a relief that you know about Leslie. I knew I had to tell you the truth before the cruise was over. I do feel better now that you know and understand."

"So do I," Selena agreed, but her mind was elsewhere and she took her leave of Julia the instant she could.

The Captain's Dinner that evening was the only meal on the cruise where the passengers were required to wear formal dress. Selena dressed with elaborate care, her stomach feeling as if there was a convention of butterflies held within its walls.

Her gown was a special one, saved for this occasion, although at the time she hadn't known this last dinner of the cruise would be specially significant in another way. It was quite likely her last evening meal with Chance.

As she walked down the grand staircase, the busboy was going through the forward cabin lounge ringing the dinner chimes. Chance was near, the base of the stairs with Julia. Selena hesitated for a split second when he glanced up, her heart pounding against her ribs. She felt the assessing sweep of his gaze and was reassured by the knowledge that her appearance was flawless.

Her dress was a filmy chiffon print of flowerets against a background of royal blue with bolder floral panels. It had a peasant neckline and billowy raglan sleeves with a long, shirred skirt. Its overall effect was totally feminine, a perfect foil for the gleaming copper of her hair.

Her heart leaped into her throat when he stepped forward to meet her. Tall and devastatingly handsome, he wore a rich black suit that emphasized his dark looks and that aura of something dangerous. There was an admiring glint in his eyes, but he offered no verbal compliment regarding her appearance.

"Shall we go down?" he addressed the question to both Selena and Julia.

"Yes," was all Selena managed. Her tongue was all tied up by her heartstrings.

It proved to be a difficulty that she couldn't overcome. She felt awkward and unsure of herself, unable to behave naturally in his presence. The champagne, courtesy of the captain, she barely sipped, afraid it would loosen the knots and let something slip.

Her silence went unnoticed, thanks to the numerous toasts by the captain and crew before dinner and the entertainment afterward thus making conversation at their table almost unnecessary. At the close of the entertainment before the dancing started, Julia made a discreet withdrawal to leave the two of them alone.

But Selena knew the kindly attempt was wasted. She was too uncomfortable and self-conscious to be alone with Chance and much, much, too aware of the way she truly felt toward him to behave as she had on previous evenings.

"Excuse me, I think I'll call it a night," she declared with a stiff smile, and rose from the table.

"Aren't you going to stay for the dancing?" he questioned mildly.

"I still have some packing to do," Selena lied. "Good night."

"Good night," Chance returned.

At the stairs leading to the cabin deck, Selena paused to glance over her shoulder. Chance had lit one of his cigars and was absently watching the smoke spiraling from the burning tip. He seemed not the least interested in her departure. It looked like a case of "out of sight, out of mind." Selena turned and walked slowly up the steps, trying to keep her head held high and not reveal how much his attitude wounded.

She wakened early the next morning. She had barely slept all night. The most she had managed was fitful dozes. Rising, she dressed and did the last of her packing, setting her luggage outside the cabin door.

There was already a line at the purser's office in the forward cabin lounge when she entered the room. Moving to the end of the line, she waited with the other passengers to settle what charges she had to pay. She saw Chance walk in and tried to ignore him as well as the crazy leaping of her heart.

His searching gaze found her in the line and he made straight for her. The boat's whistle blew the signal that it was coming in to dock. They had arrived at Cincinnati. Selena supposed Chance was coming to say goodbye and she wished he wouldn't.

When he stopped beside her, she offered a tense, "Good morning, Chance."

He didn't bother with a greeting. "I want to talk to you, Selena." His dark gaze flickered to the other passengers covertly observing their exchange. "Privately if you don't mind."

Her nerves started jumping. She didn't want to speak to him alone. She was afraid she would blurt out something that she would regret and make a terrible fool of herself in the process.

"I'd lose my place in line," she protested lamely. "Can it wait until I'm through?" Maybe then she could slip away and cowardly avoid the meeting.

"No, it can't," he insisted, eyeing her steadily.

She couldn't hold his gaze and glanced at her watch. "I don't have much time, Chance. I have a flight to catch back to Iowa."

"You can always catch a later flight." There was a hint of impatience in the line of his mouth.

"Maybe I can, but I'm not going to," she retorted.

Chance moved a step closer, his gaze narrowing in an intimidating fashion. "We are going to have this talk," he said, lowering his voice to a level of dangerous quiet. "I'll make a scene if I have to, Selena. Is that what you want?"

Compressing her lips tightly, Selena swept past him with a slightly angry toss of her head. His hand immediately clasped her elbow to guide her onto the outer deck, up the stairs to the texas deck and ultimately to his cabin.

"We can talk outside," Selena declared nervously as he inserted a key into his door lock.

"I said privately." He gently but firmly pushed her resisting figure into the cabin ahead of him, then closed the door.

Instantly she turned to face him, her pulse behaving erratically at the implied intimacy of his cabin. "All right, you've bullied me into agreeing to this conversation," she attempted to challenge him. "What is it that you have to say that can only be said in your room?"

"I simply chose a place where we couldn't be seen or overheard," he reasoned, that dark, enigmatic gaze of his studying her closely. "My cabin seemed the place that would provide that."

"What is it you want to say?" she demanded again, her breath not coming at all naturally.

97

"My aunt tells me that you've found out about Leslie and her little pretense," he stated.

"That's true," she admitted.

"And?" A dark brow lifted with a touch of arrogance.

"What do you mean—and?" Selena asked, frowning.

Chance took a minute to study the cabin key in his hand. "Don't you find her behavior a little strange?" When the question was out, he glanced at her, his eyes shuttered by a black wall.

"By strange, I suppose you mean weird or crazy." An angry hurt began building, making her voice quiver slightly. "I expect you think I'm going to condemn her behavior the way you do. Well, the truth is, Mr. Chance Barkley, that I find her little pretense unusually touching. So if you think for one minute that you've found an ally in your attempts to end these trips—and I'm presuming that is what you've been doing, rather than trying to stop an imaginary elopement—then you're very sadly mistaken. I applaud what Julia is doing and I'm going to do everything I can to encourage her to keep right on doing it. If you had an ounce of feeling for her, you'd do the same. Instead you're just a self-centered, insensitive brute who tries to bully everyone into doing what you want—"

His arms were around Selena and his mouth was crushing hers into silence before she knew what was happening. For an instant, she was rigid in his embrace, then she melted, unwilling to deny her heart what it wanted. She was breathless and shaken when he finally lifted his head.

"I only asked for an answer to my question." There was a peculiar glint in his eyes that puzzled her. "I didn't expect to receive a lecture."

His arms were still locked around her, holding her close. Finding his mouth too compellingly close for her peace of mind, Selena stared at his shirt buttons.

"Then you shouldn't treat your aunt the way you do and you wouldn't be getting any lectures," she replied defensively.

"And just how do I treat my aunt?" Chance bent his head, tipping it slightly in an effort to see her face.

"You know how you treat her," she insisted weakly. "Every time she mentioned Leslie's name on the boat, you'd go all cold and hard, totally unsympathetic to her feelings. And look at how you tried to stop her from even taking this cruise—you and your high and mighty family. You did your best to persuade her not to come. Don't forget, I was there," she finished more strongly.

His mouth twitched. "That was part of the act, Red."

Warily, she met his gaze, dark and sparkling with an inner light. "Do you mean you were only pretending that you didn't want Julia to take this cruise?"

"That's right," he nodded.

"And you came on the boat with her as—"

"No," Chance quickly corrected that delusion. "I came on the boat because of you and that little matter of the money you took from me."

"*Oh!*" Selena breathed.

"The second reason I came aboard," he continued, "was because I'd found you with Julia and the two of you were very cozy and friendly. At the time I had every reason to suspect your motives for befriending an elderly and wealthy woman."

"I suppose so," she conceded.

"As far as my reaction to Leslie's name was concerned, I didn't like the idea that Julia was involving you in her little game of make-believe. At first I thought you knew it was only a game and were going along with it. When I realized you didn't, I knew eventually you would find it out and I kept imagining what your reaction would be. Julia is very fond of you, and I didn't want to see you hurt her with any biting comments about her sanity," he explained. "Julia accuses me of being overly protective. Perhaps she's right. All I know is that I was irritated because I couldn't protect her from your ultimate discovery."

"But I don't think she's crazy for doing it," Selena protested.

"That's what she told me this morning. She said you understood her reasons, but being the cynical skeptic you've often described me as, I had to find out for myself."

"And that's why you brought me here," Selena concluded.

"That's it." His eyes smiled.

She struggled, trying to twist out of his arms. "Now that you have, you can let me go. I still have to go to the office and catch my flight." There was a catch in her voice, part of her desperate need to get away from him.

The steel band of his arms tightened the trap, keeping her in his embrace, "There's one more thing."

"What's that?" she breathed impatiently.

"Julia also told me that you're in love with me. Is that right?" he asked calmly.

Selena froze, a sickening sensation turning her stomach. "She had no right to tell you that," she choked.

"Is it true?" Chance persisted.

"Yes, it's true," she retorted, "but she had no business telling you."

"How else would I have found out?" His voice was complacent and infuriatingly calm.

"I have no idea!" Selena tried desperately to blink back the tears scalding her eyes.

"I suppose the next step is for me to fly home with you to ask your father's permission to marry you, wouldn't you say?" Chance suggested in the same composed tone.

"What?" Her head jerked up at his question, not believing she could have possibly heard correctly.

Those dark eyes were laughing silently into hers. "I hope he isn't one of those fathers who believes in long engagements. I don't think I could stand up under the strain."

Selena was still wary. "Chance, if this is your idea of a joke, I'm not going to find it very funny," she declared tightly.

"It's no joke." He stopped smiling, gazing at her so intently that she was certain he could see into her soul. "I love you and I want you to be my wife."

"Oh." The word slipped out as a bubble of happiness escaped.

"That had better be 'yes,'" he warned.

"It is!" Selena assured him, laughing and crying at the same time. "It most definitely is!"

Her arms wound around his neck as his mouth sought her lips. "Can you imagine," Chance murmured against the pliant curve of her lips, "how we're going to explain to our children the way we met? With you a minister's daughter?"

"It will be difficult," Selena laughed softly before he effectively silenced her, and not for the last time.

About the Author

Janet Dailey, who passed away in 2013, was born Janet Haradon in 1944 in Storm Lake, Iowa. She attended secretarial school in Omaha, Nebraska, before meeting her husband, Bill. The two worked together in construction and land development until they "retired" to travel throughout the United States, inspiring Janet to write the Americana series of romances, setting a novel in every state of the Union. In 1974, Janet Dailey was the first American author to write for Harlequin. Her first novel was *No Quarter Asked*. She has gone on to write approximately ninety novels, twenty-one of which have appeared on the *New York Times* bestseller list. She won many awards and accolades for her work, appearing widely on radio and television. Today, there are over three hundred million Janet Dailey books in print in nineteen different languages, making her one of the most popular novelists in the world. For more information about Janet Dailey, visit www.janetdailey.com.

OPEN ROAD
INTEGRATED MEDIA

Open Road Integrated Media is a digital publisher and multimedia content company. Open Road creates connections between authors and their audiences by marketing its ebooks through a new proprietary online platform, which uses premium video content and social media.